The Dirty Song Book

ALSO BY JERRY SILVERMAN

How to Play the Guitar
How to Play Better Guitar
Beginning the Five-String Banjo
Folk Blues
The Liberated Woman's Song Book
The Folksinger's Guitar Guide (2 volumes)
Beginning the Folk Guitar
The Art of the Folk Blues Guitar
Russian Songs
The Panic Is On
The Flat-Picker's Guitar Guide
The Folksinger's Guide to Note Reading and Music Theory
The Chord-Player's Encyclopedia
Graded Guitar
Folk Songs for Schools and Camps
That Good Old Razza Ma Tazz
Jerry Silverman's Folk Guitar Method Book
Play Old-Time Country Fiddle
Jerry Silverman's Folksong Encyclopedia
Ragtime Guitar
Folk Guitar – Folk Song

The Dirty Song Book

Jerry Silverman

S/X PRESS
New York

The artwork accompanying the songs "Uncle Fred and Auntie Mabel," "There Was an Old Farmer," and "The Friar," are from *Das Sind Unsere Lieder* published by C. Bertelsmann Verlag, and are reprinted with the permission of the artist and copyright owner, Gertrude Degenhardt.

This edition published by S/X Press,
an imprint of Marboro Books Corporation,
by arrangement with
Stein & Day/Publishers.

ISBN 0-88029-292-X
(formerly ISBN 0-8128-6118-3)

Printed in the United States of America
M 9 8 7 6

FOREWORD

Where were the folksong collectors when the dirty songs were being sung? Where were the dirty songs when Cecil Sharp, Carl Sandburg and John Lomax came around? How is it that in song after song, unearthed and preserved by these and other scholars, sexual references, when they do exist, are smoothed over and couched only in the vaguest of terms?

Consider, for example:

See what careless love has done. . .
He was her man but he done her wrong. . .
A-courtin's a pleasure. . .
Just to keep her from the foggy, foggy dew. . .

Did the cowboy, sailor, or chain-gang convict suddenly become shy when confronted with the strange fellow with the notebook (and much later, the tape recorder)? Or did the collector himself bowdlerize, expurgate, edit—and in short, "clean up" priceless and unretrievable examples of the natural wit, candor, and insight of his informants' songs?

And yet, dirty songs have always been sung. They exist in the oral tradition and are preserved through the folk process. They surface in schools, camps, military service, pubs and in so many other natural gathering places where singing plays a role that we can only infer a tacit conspiracy of silence as the reason for their almost complete non-existence in print.

Sometimes this "conspiracy" reaches unbelievably ridiculous proportions. Some years ago folksinger Burl Ives appeared on the *Ed Sullivan Show* on CBS television. Burl was noted for his performance of *The Foggy, Foggy Dew** and it was only natural that he should choose to sing it that night. I am not privy to what happened at the rehearsal of the show but it might have gone something like this:

Burl (singing): . . . *Again I am a bachelor, I live with my son . . .*
Disembodied voice over intercom: Hold it! What was that?
Burl: What was what?
DVOI: That business about a bachelor living with his son.
Burl: Yes, that's how it goes. (Sings) *Again I am a bachelor . . .*
DVOI: Wait a minute, wait a minute. You can't use that line.
Burl: But . . .
DVOI: Now Burl, baby, you know this is a family show. We can't air that "bachelor and son" stuff. Ed would blow his stack. Why do you think we showed Elvis from the waist up only? See if you can clean it up a little . . .

The result of the imaginary colloquy was a very real Burl Ives singing the following line to a waiting and watching nation which little realized how close it had come to the brink:

Burl (singing): . . . *Again I am a widower, I live with my son . . .*

And when Alec Guinness led his hardy band over the River Kwai they only whistled the tune of the so-called *Colonel Bogey March*. Do you suppose that the British soldiers didn't have some choice lyrics to fit that stirring march? You're damned right they did! Turn to page 92 for a poetical analysis of the anatomy of Hitler, Goering, Himmler, and Goebbels and then see if you could ever be satisfied just whistling the tune again.

The dirty song—the term is not a pejorative one—occupies an honorable place alongside the work song, the historical ballad, the protest song, and the love song. When cleverly constructed it is as valid a work of art as any other folksong and is subject to the same laws of survival and transmission: The good one lasts—the bad one is soon forgotten.

A good dirty song is much more than merely a series of obscenities set to music. It can be a stinging social commentary as in, *I Don't Want to Join the Army* (page 93) and *It's the Same the Whole World Over* (page 94)—an irreverent look at great figures in history, as in *Christopher Columbo* (page 40) or *The Barsted King of England* (page 22)—a roaring song of defiance, as in *Fuck 'Em All* (page 74), and *Fuk Farouk* (page 79)—an impossible tall tale, as in *Kathusalem* (page 98), or *The Fucking Machine* (page 78).

At the same time a good dirty song has to have a good singable tune. You have to be able to learn it quickly and enjoy it immediately. It is a social experience. You sing it with your friends. You enjoy it. You have fun singing it.

*Obviously not the version found in this book.

And there's the rub: Fun. Our good old Judeo-Christian-Puritan ethic tells us that we must work hard, earn our bread by the sweat of our brow, atone for the original sin, and, above all, not enjoy sex too much.

With all those guilt feelings—conscious and unconscious—that our culture instills in us on matters pertaining to sex (necessary for procreation), what must be society's "official position" on songs pertaining to sex (necessary for recreation)?

The answer is obvious. Like most "official positions": hypocritical. Damn them in the pulpit and sing them in the pub.

As a result the dirty song has existed as a kind of underground movement through the years – transmitted from singer to singer, from generation to generation despite the almost total censorship that has kept it out of our most esteemed folksong collections.

This present (im)modest volume is intended to break the chain of silence and to let the songs finally speak—and sing—for themselves.

Naturally, because of the highly specialized subject matter, a public performance of dirty songs should be handled with circumspection. As one would not ordinarily sing union songs for an audience composed of members of the National Association of Manufacturers, or black liberation songs for the Ku Klux Klan—try to avoid performing these delicate ditties for the Campfire Girls, Daughters of the American Revolution, Parent-Teacher Associations, and United Jewish Appeal fund-raising dinners. Individual members of these groups may, on the other hand, be quite responsive to this material and might even surprise you with a few good songs of their own.* If you have the good fortune to come across a worthwhile dirty song in this or any other manner, won't you share it with the rest of us? Send it to me c/o Stein and Day/*Publishers*. When we have enough songs for volume two we may publish another book and if I use it I'll send you a free copy.

Jerry Silverman

*For example, a five-year old student of mine supplied me with the following:

I see your tushy,
It's soft and mushy.
You better hide it
Before I bite it.

FOREPIECE

Dirty Songs Are Good For You!

Actually this is a paraphrase of a remark made by Professor Gottfried von Drecken while discussing his definitive monograph, *Das Schmutzige Lied: Was Ist Das?*,[1] at the annual convention of *Die Gesellschaft für Muzikwissenschaft*, held at Baden-Baden in August 1908. Musicologists, scholars, and neo-pornographers had flocked to the famous spa in hopes of hearing von Drecken—then at the height of his creative powers—offer some new insight into the delicate *demimonde* of *"das schmutzige Lied"*—the dirty song, or *"Schmutzis,"* as they would soon come to be called.

Baden-Baden was a fortuitous choice for the convention. For this was no ordinary gathering of savants who confined their research to dusty archives and crumbling manuscripts of long forgotten poets and composers. No! These men and women were active, tireless, dedicated field workers who had spent many sleepless nights in the pursuit of the elusive *Schmutzie*. The convention sites committee of the society had chosen well: The curative waters of Baden-Baden would revitalize and restore their tired members.

They were all there that hot afternoon on the shady veranda of the Grand Hotel excitedly discussing the *"von Drecken Papier"* and sipping their deliciously chilled lemonade: Le Comte de Morpion and Professeur Braguette of the Acadamie Française; Sir Archibald Ballock and Lady Fitz-Tightly of the Royal Academy (co-authors of the sensational *Scottish Buggery Balladry, or Lying Low in the Highlands*[2]); the Dutchman, van der Petzel (last year's *cause célèbre*: his analysis, *Some New Insights on the Boy Who Stuck His Finger into the Dike; or Flying High in the Lowlands*[3]); a large delegation from Bohemia (there always seemed to be a great many Bohemians at these conventions); the Viennese, Schwantz, who had just returned from five years in the Australian outback with a wealth of material on Aboriginal castration chants (gathered first hand and expounded upon in that curious falsetto of his); Dr. Ebenezer Kinsey, the American lexicographer and folklorist (*"Folk"—A Four-Letter Word: Accident or Design?*[4]). . . and many others from all over the world.

In the center of this large crowd, holding court, as it were, and enjoying every minute of it was von Drecken, himself. He had a particular fondness in those days for chocolate eclairs, and between sips of lemonade and words of greeting to his friends and colleagues he was putting away an enormous quantity of those crème-filled pastries.

He seemed to be eyeing the doorway leading onto the veranda from the hotel as if he were expecting someone. "He's waiting for the Chinese delegate. It's his old friend Tee Song, with whom he studied at the University of Shanghai," whispered Sir Archibald to his neighbor, Braguette. "You remember Tee Song—*The Lacquered Boxes of the Empresses' Ladies-In-Waiting.*"[5]

Suddenly there was a commotion near the entrance. Gretchen, the plump young blonde waitress who had been putting clean silverware into the lowest drawer of the serving table straightened up quickly with a loud gasp, scattering a handful of forks on the tile floor, as an Oriental gentleman walked briskly past.

It was, of course, Tee Song, and von Drecken spotted him immediately. Stuffing the remaining two-thirds of an eclair into his mouth von Drecken swiftly rose from the table to greet his old comrade.

The two men advanced toward each other, arms outspread in recognition. It was von Drecken who spoke first as they embraced. "Dear Tee Song," he mumbled in his heavily accented English—half choking as he tried to swallow his eclair. "Dear Tee Song, ach, good for you!"

The Reuters man who was discreetly studying his menu at a nearby table could scarcely believe what he thought he had heard. He took out his pencil and hastily scribbled it down on his napkin. As soon as he could he slipped away to the telegraph office and sent the following message to his London bureau and thence to the waiting world: "Von Drecken says, 'Dirty songs are good for you!'"

1. *Zeitschrift für Muzikwissenschaft II*, (1909), pp. 362-375.
2. *Musica Brittanica*, (1907), pp. 101-145.
3. *Vereniging vor Nederlands Muziekgeschiedenis I*, (1908), pp. 23-38.
4. *University of Kansas City Press*, (1906), Illustrated.
5. From his *I-li, or Book of Etiquette and Ceremonial*, appearing in the *North-China Branch of the Royal Asiatic Society* XXXIV, (1904). Also known as *Erotica in Exotica, ibid.*

CONTENTS

The Dirty Song Book

ACT SEDERUNT OF THE SESSION

In Scottish law, an "Act Sederunt" is a piece of general legislation.

By **ROBERT BURNS**

Verse:
G D Em C
In Ed - in - burgh town they've made a law, In
G D G D G D
Ed - in - burgh at the Court o' Ses - sion, That stand - ing pricks are
Em C G D G D
fau - teors a', And guilt - y of a high trans - gres - sion.
Chorus:
Em C G Em A7 D
Act Se - der - unt o' the Ses - sion, De - creet o' the Court o' Ses - sion, That
G D Em C G D G D
stand - ing pricks are fau - teors, a', And guilt - y of a high trans - gres - sion.


```
            G    D        Em         C
And they've provided dungeons deep.
    G        D     G       D
Ilk lass has ane in her possession:
    G          D       Em         C
Until the wretches wail and weep,
         G        D        G             D
There shall they lie for their transgression.
```

```
           Em              C       G
Chorus:  Act Sederunt o' the Session,
             Em          A7        D
         Decreet o' the Court o' Session;
                 G          D        Em          C
         The rogues in pouring tears shall weep,
               G   D          G       D
         By Act Sederunt o' the Session.
```

Glossary

fauteors a'	offenders all
Ilk lass has ane	every lass has one

ABDUL THE BULBUL EMIR

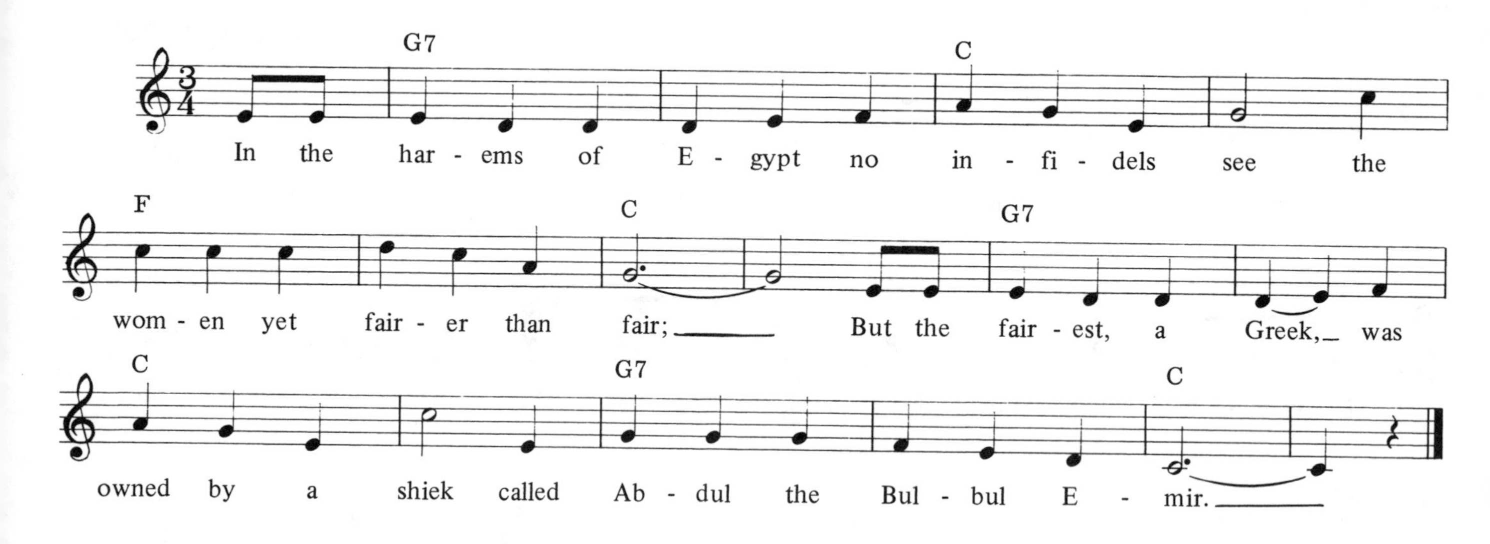

G7
C
In the har - ems of E - gypt no in - fi - dels see the
F
C
G7
wom - en yet fair - er than fair; But the fair - est, a Greek, was
C
G7
C
owned by a shiek called Ab - dul the Bul - bul E - mir.

G7 C
A traveling brothel came into the town,
F C
Run by a pimp from afar
G7 C
So great was its fame that well-known was the name
G7 C
Of Ivan Skavinsky Skavar.

G7 C
Abdul the Bulbul arrived with his bride,
F C
A prize whose eyes shone like a star.
G7 C
He claimed he could prong more cunts with his dong
G7 C
Than Ivan Skavinsky Skavar.

G7 C
A great fucking contest was set for the day
F C
A visit was planned by the czar,
G7 C
And the curbs were all lined with harlots reclined
G7 C
In honor of Ivan Skavar.

G7 C
They met on the track with their tools hanging slack,
F C
Dressed only in shoes and a leer.
G7 C
Both were fast on the rise, but they gasped at the size
G7 C
Of Abdul the Bulbul Emir.

G7 C
They worked through the night till the dawn's early light.
F C
The clamor was heard from afar.
G7 C
The multitudes came to applaud the ball game
G7 C
Of Abdul and Ivan Skavar.

G7 C
The cunts were all shorn and no rubbers adorned
F C
The prongs of the pimp and the peer,
G7 C
But the pimp's steady stroke all the chances soon broke
G7 C
Of Abdul the Bulbul Emir.

G7 C
When Ivan had finished he turned to the Greek
F C
And laughed when she shook with great fear.
G7 C
She swallowed his pride; he buggered the bride
G7 C
Of Abdul the Bulbul Emir.

G7 C
When Ivan was done and was wiping his gun,
F C
He bent down to polish his gear.
G7 C
He felt up his ass a hard pecker pass;
G7 C
'Twas Abdul the Bulbul Emir.

G7 C
Now the crowds looking on proclaimed who had won.
F C
They were ordered to part by the czar.
G7 C
But fast were they jammed. The pecker was crammed
G7 C
In Ivan Skavinsky Skavar.

G7 C
Now the cream of the joke when apart they were broke
F C
Was laughed at for years by the czar,
G7 C
For Abdul the Bulbul left most of his tool
G7 C
In Ivan Skavinsky Skavar.

G7 C
The fair Grecian maiden a sad vigil keeps
F C
With a husband whose tastes have turned queer.
G7 C
She longs for the dong that once did belong
G7 C
To Abdul the Bulbul Emir.

ALI BOOGIE

Tempo di boogie
E
I boo - gied last night, and the night be - fore, I'm
go - ing back to - night and___ boo - gie some more.
E7
Chorus:
A7
A - li boo - gie___ is all I crave.___ For
E
B7
good old A - li boo - gie will drive me to my grave.___
A7
for repeats
E A7 E B7
Final ending
E A7 E E7

E
Momma's on the bottom, poppa's on top,
E7
Baby's in the attic filling rubbers with snot. *Chorus*

E
Momma's on the bottom, poppa's on top,
E7
Baby's in the cradle yelling, "Shove it to 'er, Pop!" *Chorus*

E
Momma's in the hospital, poppa's in jail,
E7
Sister's in the corner crying, "Pussy for sale!" *Chorus*

E
I got a gal about six-foot-four,
E7
She fucks everything like a two-bit whore. *Chorus*

E
I got a gal lives on the hill,
E7
She won't do it but her sister will. *Chorus*

E
Daddy's got a watch, momma's got a ring;
E7
Sister's got a baby from shaking that thing. *Chorus*

E
One and one makes two – two and two makes four,
E7
If the bed breaks down we'll fuck on the floor. *Chorus*

A LITTLE BIT OFF THE TOP

Tune: **WHEN JOHNNY COMES MARCHING HOME**

Em G
When I was eight days old, my boys, hur - rah, hur - rah,
Em
When I was eight days old, my boys, hur -
G B7 Em
rah, hur - rah The rab - bi came with a
Am Em B7
big sharp knife, And I sure - ly thought he would take my life, But
Em D C B7 Em Am Em
all he took was a lit - tle bit off the top.

```
Em                              G
O, that is what they call a bris, hurrah, hurrah.
Em                              G       B7
O, that is what they call a bris, hurrah, hurrah.
 Em              Am
And if the rabbi doesn't miss,
Em                    B7
It makes for a more interesting piss,
   Em D  C   B7   Em      Am      Em
But all he took was a little bit off the top.
```

```
       Em                        G
The rabbi, he is called a moyl, hurrah, hurrah,
       Em                        G       B7
The rabbi, he is called a moyl, hurrah, hurrah.
    Em          Am
And over me he sure did toil,
       Em                         B7
If he'd cut off more, I'd have been a goil,
     Em D C    B7    Em      Am      Em
But all he took was a little bit off the top.
```

```
         Em                    G
O, circumcision is all right, hurrah, hurrah,
         Em                    G       B7
O, circumcision is all right, hurrah, hurrah.
        Em                 Am
But every morning and every night,
      Em              B7
You aim to the left and pee to the right,
     Em D  C  B7   Em     Am     Em
But all he took was little bit off the top.
```

A-ROVIN'

D A7 D A7 D A7
In Am - ster - dam there lived a maid, Mark well what I do
D G D
say. In Am - ster - dam there lived a maid, And
Em E7 A7 D
she was mis - tress of her trade. I'll go no more a -
G D A7 D Chorus: G
rov - in' with you fair maid. A - rov - in', a -
D Em E7 A7
rov - in', since rov - in's been my ru - i - in. And I'll
D G D A7 D
go no more a - rov - in' with you fair maid.

D A7 D A7
I put my hand upon her knee.
D A7 D
Mark well what I do say.
G D
I put my hand upon her knee.
Em E7 A7
She said, "Young man, you're rather free."
D G D A7 D
I'll go no more a-rovin' with you, fair maid. *Chorus*

D A7 D A7
I put my hand upon her thigh.
D A7 D
Mark well what I do say.
G D
I put my hand upon her thigh.
Em E7 A7
She said, "Young man, you're rather high."
D G D A7 D
I'll go no more a-rovin' with you, fair maid. *Chorus*

D A7 D A7
I put my hand upon her snatch.
D A7 D
Mark well what I do say.
G D
I put my hand upon her snatch.
Em E7 A7
She said, "Young man, that's my main hatch."
D G D A7 D
I'll go no more a-rovin' with you, fair maid. *Chorus*

D A7 D A7
She rolled me over on my back.
D A7 D
Mark well what I do say.
G D
She rolled me over on my back
Em E7 A7
And fucked so hard my balls did crack.
D G D A7 D
I'll go no more a-rovin' with you, fair maid. *Chorus*

```
        D       A7          D          A7
And then I slipped her on the blocks.
        D         A7    D
Mark well what I do say.
       G                    D
And then I slipped her on the blocks.
     Em                          E7       A7
She said, "Young man, I've got the pox."
     D                    G          D    A7   D
I'll go no more a-rovin' with you, fair maid. Chorus
```

```
        D          A7           D              A7
And when she spent my whole year's pay,
        D        A7     D
Mark well what I do say.
        G                  D
And when she spent my whole year's pay,
        Em                         E7       A7
She slipped her anchor and sailed away.
     D                    G          D    A7   D
I'll go no more a-rovin' with you, fair maid. Chorus
```

A LUSTY YOUNG SMITH

Lustily
D A7 D
A lust - y young smith at his forge stood a - fil - ing, His ham - mer laid
Em A G D
by but his forge still a - glow, When to him a bux - om young
A7 D Bm A7
dam - sel came smil - ing, And asked if to work at her forge he would
D Chorus: D A7
go. With a jin - gle, bang, jin - gle, bang, jin - gle, bang,
D A7 D
jin - gle. With a jin - gle, bang, jin - gle, bang, jin - gle, hi - ho!

"I will," said the smith, and they went off together,
Along to the young damsel's forge they did go.
They stripped to go to it, 'twas hot work and hot weather;
She kindled a fire and she soon made him glow. *Chorus*

Her husband, she said, no good work could afford her;
His strength and his tools were worn out long ago.
The smith said, "Well, mine are in very good order,
And now I am ready my skill for to show." *Chorus*

Red hot grew his iron, as both did desire,
And he was too wise not to strike while 'twas so.
Quoth she, "What I get, I get out of the fire,
Then prithee, strike home and redouble the blow." *Chorus*

Six times did his iron, by vigorous heating.
Grow soft in the forge in a minute or so
And often was hardened, still beating and beating,
But the more it was softened, it hardened more slow. *Chorus*

The smith then would go; quoth the dame, full of sorrow,
"Oh, what would I give, could my husband do so!
Good lad, with your hammer come hither tomorrow —
But, pray, can't you use it once more, ere you go?" *Chorus*

A RIDDLE

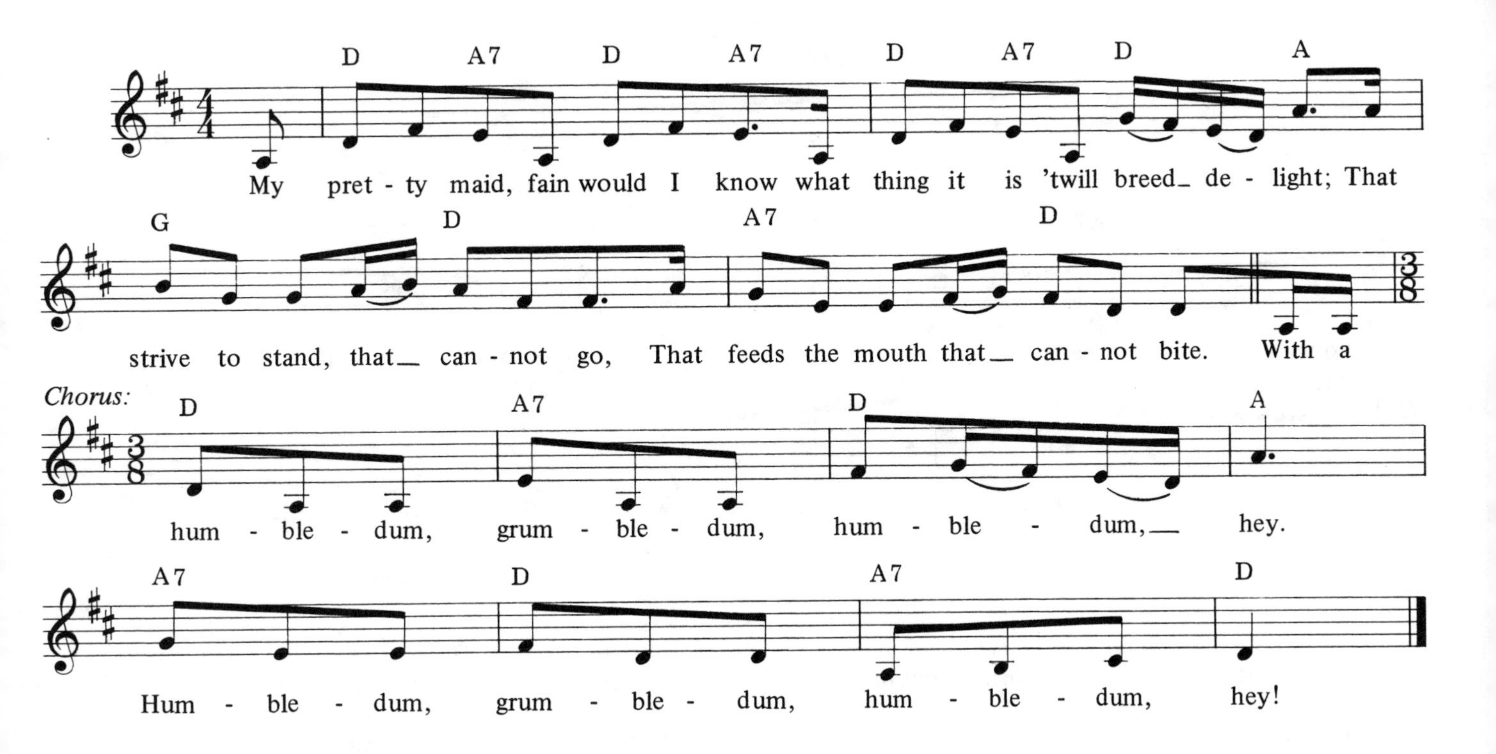
D A7 D A7 D A7 D A
My pret - ty maid, fain would I know what thing it is 'twill breed_ de - light; That
G D A7 D
strive to stand, that_ can - not go, That feeds the mouth that_ can - not bite. With a
Chorus:
D A7 D A
hum - ble - dum, grum - ble - dum, hum - ble - dum,_ hey.
A7 D A7 D
Hum - ble - dum, grum - ble - dum, hum - ble - dum, hey!

D A7 D A7
It is a pretty pricking thing,
D A7 D A
A pleasing and a standing thing;
G D
It was the truncheon Mars did use.
A7 D
A bedward bit that maidens choose. *Chorus*

D A7 D A7
It is a friar with a bald head,
D A7 D A
A staff to beat a cuckold dead;
G D
It is a gun that shoots point-blank,
A7 D
It hits betwixt a maiden's flank. *Chorus*

D A7 D A7
It is a shaft of Cupid's cut,
D A7 D A
'Twill served to rove, to prick, to butt;
G D
'Twas ne'er a maid but by her will
A7 D
Will keep it in her quiver still. *Chorus*

D A7 D A7
It has a head much like a mole's
D A7 D A
And yet it loves to creep in holes.
G D
The fairest maid that e'er took life
A7 D
For love of this became a wife. *Chorus*

A WANTON TRICK

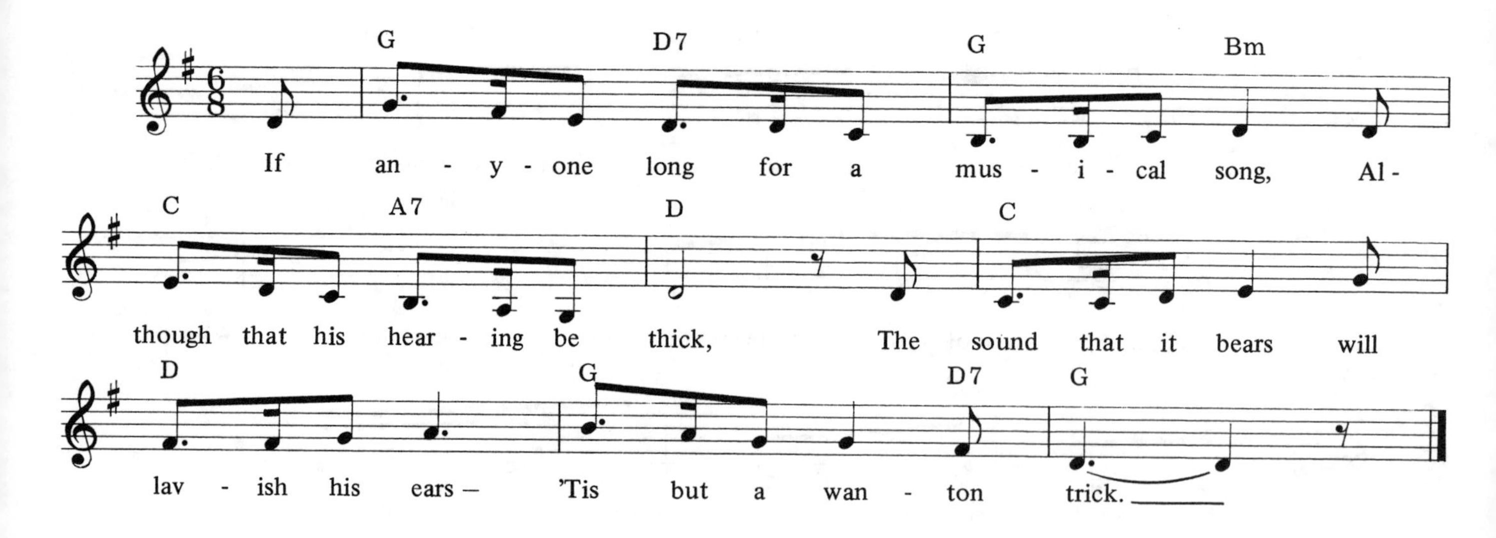
G D7 G Bm
If an - y - one long for a mus - i - cal song, Al -
C A7 D C
though that his hear - ing be thick, The sound that it bears will
D G D7 G
lav - ish his ears – 'Tis but a wan - ton trick.

G D7 G Bm
A pleasant young maid on an instrument played
C A7 D
That knew neither note nor prick.
C D
She had a good will to live by her skill –
G D7 G
'Tis but a wanton trick.

G D7 G Bm
A youth in that art, well seen in his part,
C A7 D
They called him Darbyshire Dick,
C D
Came to her a suitor and would be her tutor –
G D7 G
'Tis but a wanton trick.

G D7 G Bm
He pleased her so well that backward she fell
C A7 D
And swooned as though she were sick.
C D
So sweet was his note that up went her coat –
G D7 G
'Tis but a wanton trick.

G D7 G Bm
The string of his viol she put to the trial
C A7 D
'Til she had the full length of the stick.
C D
Her white-bellied lute she set to his flute –
G D7 G
'Tis but a wanton trick.

G D7 G Bm
Thus she with her lute and he with his flute
C A7 D
Held every crotchet and prick.
C D
She learned at her leisure yet paid for her pleasure –
G D7 G
'Tis but a wanton trick.

G D7 G Bm
His viol string burst, her tutor she cursed;
C A7 D
However, she played with the stick.
C D
From October to June she was quite out of tune –
G D7 G
'Tis but a wanton trick.

G D7 G Bm
And then she repented that e'er she consented
C A7 D
To have either note or prick;
C D
For learning so well made her belly to swell –
G D7 G
'Tis but a wanton trick.

G D7 G Bm
All maids that make trial of a lute or a viol,
C A7 D
Take heed how you handle the stick;
C D
If you like not this order, come, try my recorder –
G D7 G
'Tis but a wanton trick.

A YOUNG MAN AND HIS MAID

Lyrically
Em
Am Em
A young man and his maid, put in all, put in all, To -
B7 Em
geth - er late - ly played, put in all. The young man was in jest, O, the
Am B7 Em C B7 Em
maid she did pro - test. She bid him do his best, put in all, put in all.

Em Am Em
With that her rolling eyes, put in all, put in all,
B7
Turned upward to the skies, put in all.
Em
The young man was in heat,
Am B7
The maid did soundly sweat;
Em C
A little farther get
B7 Em
Put in all, put in all.

Em Am Em
When they had ended sport, put in all, put in all,
B7
She found him all too short, put in all.
Em
For when he'd done his best
Am B7
The maid she did protest
Em C
'Twas nothing but a jest,
B7 Em
Put in all, put in all.

Em Am Em
According to her will, put in all, put in all,
B7
The young man tried his skill, put in all,
Em
But the proverb plain does tell,
Am B7
That, use them ne'er so well,
Em C
For an inch they'd take an ell,
B7 Em
Put in all, put in all.

THE BALLAD OF AIMEE McPHERSON

A true story about the mysterious disappearance and reappearance of the California evangelist in 1926.

Em D C B7
Did you ev - er hear the sto - ry of
Aim - ee Mc - Pher - son? Aim - ee Mc - Pher - son, that
Em B7
won - der - ful per - son, She weighed a hun - dred eight - y and her
hair was red, And preached a wick - ed ser - mon, so the
Em Chorus: C Em A♯dim Em
pa - pers said. Hi dee hi dee hi dee hi. Ho dee ho dee ho dee ho.

B7
Aimee built herself a radio station,
Em
To broadcast her preaching to the nation.
B7
Found a man named Armistad who knew enough
Em
To run the radio while Aimee did her stuff. *Chorus*

B7
Started at a camp meeting down at Ocean Park,
Em
Preached from early morning till after dark.
B7
Said the benediction, folded up the tent,
Em
And nobody knew where Aimee went. *Chorus*

B7
When Aimee McPherson got back from her journey,
Em
She told her story to the district attorney.
B7
Said she'd been kidnapped on a lonely trail,
Em
And in spite of a lot of questions she stuck to her tale. *Chorus*

```
       B7
The grand jury started an investigation;
                          Em
Uncovered a lot of spicy information.
        B7
Found out about her love nest down at Carmel-by-the-sea,
                                        Em
Where the likker is expensive and the loving is free. Chorus

  B7
Found a little cottage with a breakfast nook,
                      Em
A folding bed with a worn out look.
      B7
The slats was busted and the springs was loose,
                                       Em
And the dents in the mattress fitted Aimee's caboose. Chorus

      B7
They took poor Aimee and they threw her in jail,
                   Em
Last I heard she was out on bail.
          B7
They'll send her up for a stretch, I guess
                                Em
She worked herself up into an awful mess. Chorus

  B7
Radio Ray* is a going hound,
                        Em
He's a-going yet and he can't be found
        B7
They got his description but they got it too late,
                                     Em
Cause since they got it he's lost a lot of weight. Chorus

     B7
I'll end my story in the usual way,
                      Em
About a lady preacher's holiday
   B7
If you don't get the moral, then you're the gal for me,
                                               Em
Cause there's still a lot of cottages down by Carmel on-the-sea. Chorus
```

*Ray Armistad, Aimee's radio announcer and alleged lover.

THE BALL OF BALLYMOOR

(Also Known as "The Ball of Kerrimuir")

Verse:
D
I'll sing you a song of the Ball of Bal - ly - moor,
G D E7
Four and twen - ty pros - ti - tutes a - ly - ing on the
A
floor.
Chorus:
D
Sing - ing who hae ye last nicht, And
who hae ye noo? The
G
man wha' hae ye
D A7 D
last nicht, he can - na hae ye noo.

D
There was fucking in the kitchen,

There was fucking in the halls.
G D
You couldna hear the music
E7 A
For the clanking of the balls. *Chorus*

D
There was fucking in the parlor,

There was fucking in the ricks.
G D
You couldna hear the music
E7 A
For the swishing of the pricks. *Chorus*

D
The minister's wife was at the ball,

A-sitting in the front;
G D
A wreath of flowers 'round her ass,
E7 A
A carrot up her cunt. *Chorus*

D
The queen was in the kitchen

Eating bread and honey.
G D
The king was in the chambermaid,
E7 A
And she was in the money. *Chorus*

```
            D
There was fucking in the bedrooms,

There was fucking on the stairs.
      G               D
You couldna see the carpet
          E7              A
For the piles of pubic hairs. Chorus

D
First lady forward,

Second lady pass.
G           D
Third lady's finger
          E7          A
Up the fourth lady's ass. Chorus

      D
The bride was in the parlor,

Explaining to the groom
           G                D
That the vagina, not the rectum,
      E7                  A
Is the entrance to the womb. Chorus

      D
The groom was all excited,

And racing 'round the halls.
    G               D
A-stumbling on his pecker
      E7                A
And a-tripping o'er his balls. Chorus

D
The collier delegation came,

But soon they got the boot;
  G                D
For every time they farted,
     E7                    A
They filled the room with soot. Chorus

         D
In the middle of the ballroom

The village idiot sat,
 G                    D
Amusing himself by abusing himself,
     E7              A
And catching it in his hat. Chorus

     D
The elders of the church

Who were far to old to firk
   G            D
All sat around the table,
             E7          A
Where they had a circle jerk. Chorus

            D
And when the ball was over,

This opinion was expressed:
   G           D
The music was delightful,
        E7              A
But the fucking was the best. Chorus
```

BALLS TO MISTER BANGLESTEIN

Freely
C G7 C
There was an old monk of great re - nown, there
G7 C F C
was an old monk of great re - nown, There was an old monk of
G7 C Em
great re - nown, And he fucked the wom - en all
G G7 Chorus:
o - ver the town. (Spoken:) The sod, the dirty old sod, The bastard deserves to die. Have mercy on his soul. Fuck him!
C G G7 C a tempo
Glo - ry, glo - ry hal - le - lu - jah. Balls to Mis - ter
G7 C
Ban - gle - stein, Ban - gle - stein, Ban - gle - stein. Balls to Mis - ter Ban - gle - stein,
G7 C G7 C G7
dir - ty old sod. For he keeps us wait - ing while he's mas - tur -
C G7 C
bat - ing. Balls to Mis - ter Ban - gle - stein, dir - ty old sod.

```
    C                  G7      C
The other monks cried out in shame,
                       G7      C
The other monks cried out in shame,
    F      C           G7      C
The other monks cried out in shame,
      Em                      G              G7
So he turned around and he fucked them again.
```
Chorus

```
    C                   G7         C
The other monks grew tired of his frolics,
                        G7         C
The other monks grew tired of his frolics,
    F      C            G7         C
The other monks grew tired of his frolics,
        Em                     G             G7
So they took a knife and they cut off his ballocks.
```
Chorus

THE BALHAM VICAR

There once was a Bal - ham vic - ar, who said to his cu - rate,
John: "I'll bet I've fucked more wom - en than you," And the cu - rate said, "You're
on, you're on." And the cu - rate said, "You're on." Well, we'll stand out - side the
church this day, and this will be our sign: You "ding - a - ding" for the
wom - en you've fucked, And I'll "dong - a - dong" for mine, for mine, And
I'll "dong - a - dong" for mine. Well, there were more "ding - a - dings" and
"dong - a - dong dongs," till a pret - ty young bird come by, And the
cu - rate went "Ding ding." "Oh," said the vic - ar, "Don't ding - a - ding there.
That's my wife I do de - clare,"
Guitar tacet
Spoken:
"Hell," said the cu - rate, "I don't care.
Ding - a - ding - a - ding, ding, ding, ding, ding, Ding - a - ding - a - ding, ding, dong."

BANG AWAY, LULU

C
D7
I wish I was a dia - mond up - on my Lu - lu's
G7
hand, And ev - 'ry time she wiped her ass, I'd see the prom - ised
C
Chorus:
D7
land. Oh, — Bang a - way, my Lu - lu, Bang a - way good and strong. Oh,
G7
C
What - 'll we do for a good old screw when Lu - lu's dead and gone?


```
C                      D7
I wish I was the pee-pot, beneath my Lulu's bed,
   G7                                         C
For every time she took a piss, I'd see her maidenhead. Chorus
```

```
  C                  D7
My Lulu had a baby. She named it Sunny Jim.
     G7                                    C
She dropped in in the pee-pot to see if he could swim. Chorus
```

```
 C                              D7
First it went to the bottom, and then it came to the top,
         G7                                C
Then my Lulu got excited and grabbed it by the cock. Chorus
```

```
  C                   D7
I wish I was a candle, within my Lulu's room,
    G7                                          C
And every night at nine o'clock, I'd penetrate her womb. Chorus
```

```
  C                          D7
My Lulu's tall and sprightly. My Lulu's tall and thin.
  G7                                                   C
I caught her by the railroad track jacking off with a coupling-pin. Chorus
```

```
  C                       D7
My Lulu was arrested; ten dollars was the fine.
    G7                                         C
She said to the judge, "Take it out of this ass of mine." Chorus
```

```
        C                                   D7
Sometimes I got a nickel and sometimes I got a dime,
      G7                                       C
But when I got a quarter, Lulu lays it on the line. Chorus
```

```
 C                        D7
Pappy loved my mammy; mammy loved the men.
      G7                                        C
Now mammy's full of buckshot and pappy's in the pen. Chorus
```

```
 C                   D7
Lulu got religion; she had it once before.
      G7                                                    C
She prayed to Christ with the minister while they did it on the floor. Chorus
```

```
    C                            D7
My Lulu went to Boston, and there she met a trucker,
      G7                                                          C
She high-balled to the bedroom cryin', "Double-clutch me, mother-fucker." Chorus
```

```
    C                    D7
My Lulu had a sister who lived up on a hill.
       G7                                     C
If she hadn't died of syphilis, we'd be banging still. Chorus
```

```
  C                         D7
Some girls work in offices; some girls work in stores,
     G7                                       C
But Lulu works in a hotel with forty other whores. Chorus
```

THE BARSTED KING OF ENGLAND

With gusto
Verse:
C
Oh, the min - strels sing of an Eng - lish king of
F C G7
man - y long years a - go, Who ruled his land with an
C F C
i - ron hand, Though his mor - als were weak and low. He
F C
loved to hunt the roy - al stag That lived in the roy - al wood; But
G7 C F C
bet - ter than it he loved to sit And pound the roy - al pud.
Chorus:
F C
All wild and wool - y and cov - ered with fleas, His ter - ri - ble tool hung
G7 C Am Em Am D7 G7 C
down to his knees. God save the bar - sted King of Eng - land.

C
The Queen of Spain was an amorous Jane,
F C
A lascivious wench was she.
G7
She loved to fool with the barsted's tool,
C F C
So far across the sea.

So she sent a special message
F C
By a special messenger,
G7
To ask the king if he would spend
C F C
A night or two with her.

F
Chorus: He was wild and woolly and full of fleas,
C G7
And he had his women by twos and threes.
C Am Em Am D7 G7 C
God save the barsted King of Eng - land.

C
When Phillip of France he heard of this,
F
He summoned the royal court.
G7
He swore, "She loves my rival more
C F C
Because my tool is short!"

His ministerial council
F C
Said it was a grave affront.
G7
King Phillip said, "God strike me dead,
C F C
I'll fix her royal cunt!"

F
Chorus: He sent for the Duke of Zippety Zap,
C G7
To give the Queen a dose of the clap,
C Am Em Am D7 G7 C
To give to the barsted King of Eng - land.

C
When the barsted King he heard of this,
F C
All in fair England's walls,
G7
He took an oath by his hairy growth,
C F C
He'd have the Frenchman's balls.

So he offered half his kingdom,
C F C
And a piece of Queen Hortense
G7
To any man with a ten-inch span
C F C
Who'd diddle the King of France.

F
Chorus: A volunteer it soon was found,
C G7
Who's size of prize it was renowned,
C Am Em Am D7 G7 C
To serve well the barsted King of Eng - land.

C
The royal Duke of Buttocks
F C
Betook himself to France.
G7
He swore he was a fruiter,
C F C
So King Phillip pulled down his pants.

But at the crucial moment,
F C
Now, here's the best of all,
G7
As Phillip leapt, the Duke sidestepped
C F C
And seized the royal ball.

F
Chorus: Around his dong he slipped a thong,
C G7
Jumped on his horse and dragged him along,
C Am Em Am D7 G7 C
Back to the barsted King of Eng - land.

(continued)

        C
But when he reached fair England's shores
             F   C
He fainted on the floor.
    G7
For on the ride King Phillip's pride
      C   F   C
Got stretched out six times more.

The maids from all the countryside,
                 F   C
They gathered in the town.
      G7
They took one look at the Frenchman's crook,
          C   F   C
And denounced the royal crown.

                 F
Chorus: They set King Phillip upon the throne,
      C   G7
His scepter is the royal bone.
 C   Am   Em   Am   D7 G7 C
Farewell, the barsted King of Eng - land.

THE BAND PLAYED ON

G Gmaj7 G6 G Gdim
Ca - sey got hit with a buck - et of shit and the
D7 Am7 D7 Am7 D7
band played on. He waltzed 'round the floor and got hit with some
G
more and the band played on. His balls were so
D7 G7 C E7
load - ed, they near - ly ex - plod - ed, The poor girl she
Am C C♯dim
shook with a - larm. He mar - ried the bitch with the
G B7 Em A7 D7 G
sev - en - year itch, And the band played on.

BELL-BOTTOM TROUSERS

British Version

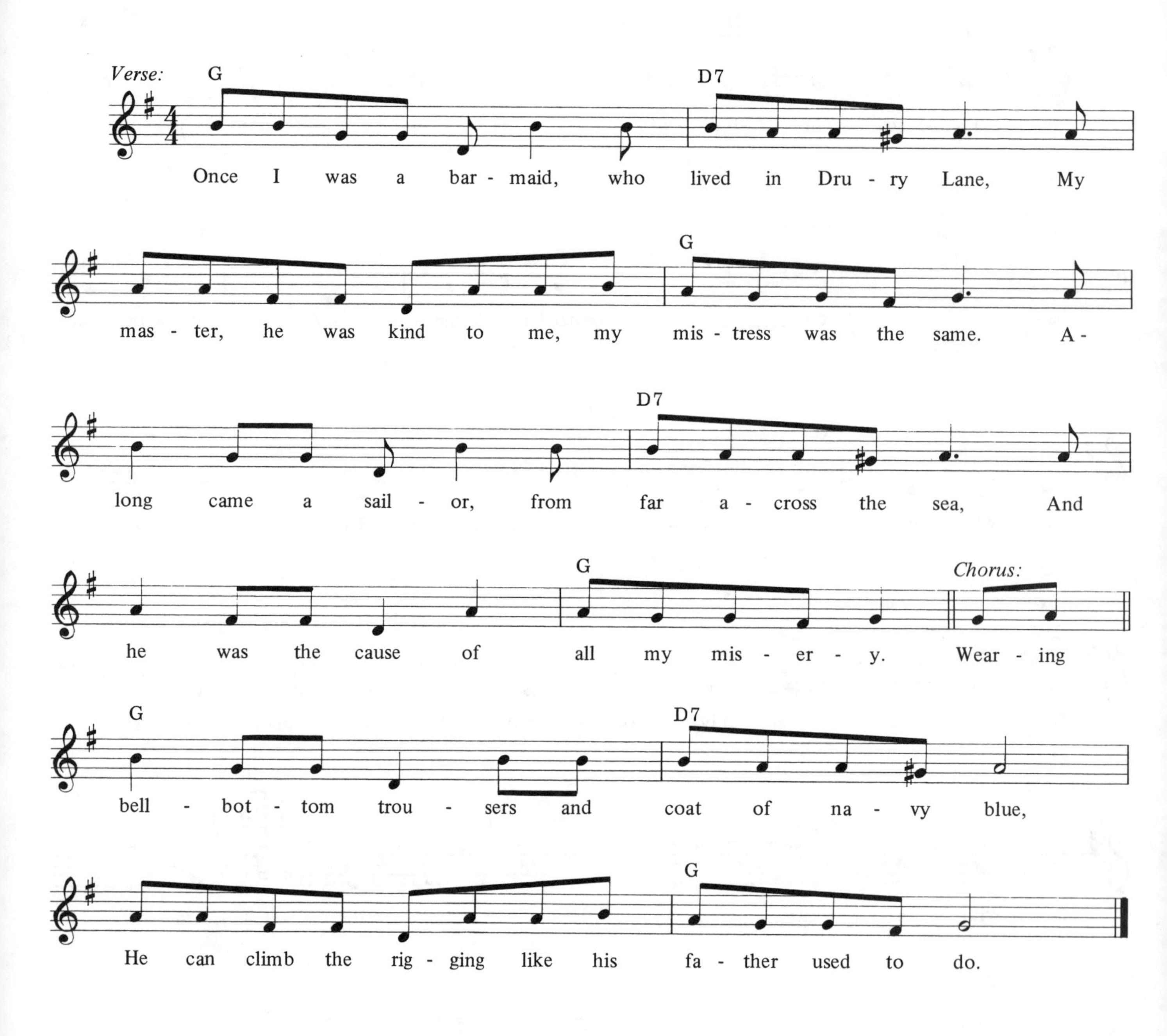
Verse:
G
D7
Once I was a bar - maid, who lived in Dru - ry Lane, My
G
mas - ter, he was kind to me, my mis - tress was the same. A -
D7
long came a sail - or, from far a - cross the sea, And
G
Chorus:
he was the cause of all my mis - er - y. Wear - ing
G
D7
bell - bot - tom trou - sers and coat of na - vy blue,
G
He can climb the rig - ging like his fa - ther used to do.

```
       G                   D7
He asked me for a candle to light his way to bed,
                           G
He asked me for a kerchief to cover up his head.
                           D7
And I being a simple maid and thinking it no harm,
                             G
Climbed into the sailor's bed to keep the sailor warm. Chorus
```

```
       G                   D7
Now, early in the morning, just at the break of day,
                                    G
He handed me a five-pound note and this to me did say,
                             D7
"Take this, my darling, for the damage I have done,
                                    G
Maybe you'll have a daughter and maybe you'll have a son." Chorus
```

Sung to the melody of the chorus

```
     G                     D7
"And if you have a daughter, bounce her on your knee,
                                    G
And if you have a son, dear, send the bastard out to sea." Chorus
```

```
         G                 D7
Now the moral of this story is very plain to see;
                     G
Never trust a sailor an inch above your knee.
                     D7
Once I trusted one and now just look at me,
                          G
I've got a little bastard a-bouncing on my knee. Chorus
```

American Version

```
     G                       D7
Once I was young and happy, it was my heart's delight
                             G
To go to balls and parties and stay out late at night.
                             D7
It was at a ball one evening, he asked me for a dance;
                           G
I knew he was a sailor by the buttons on his pants. Chorus
```

```
     G                               D7
He danced with me all evening and asked to take me home,
                                         G
His shoes were brightly polished and his hair was neatly combed.
                                  D7
It was on my father's doorstep where I was led astray,
                                  G
It was in my mother's bedroom where I was forced to lay. Chorus
```

(continued)

G   D7
When nine months came and passed a son was born to me.
                                          G
He looked just like his father, and filled my heart with glee.
                              D7
He grew to be a sailor and sailed the seven seas,
                                                G
And he knocked up a girl in Boston like his daddy did to me. *Chorus*

G   D7
Now, all you pretty maidens, just take a tip from me,
                         G
Never trust a sailor an inch above your knee.
                                              D7
He will love you and caress you and he'll say that he'll be true,
                                        G
But once he's got your cherry, it's gone to hell with you. *Chorus*

Sperm is fattening. (New York City subway graffito)

BIBLE STORY

A Dramatic Narration

'Twas the night of the royal castration—or, it wasn't the first time a royal ball was being pulled. The king ordered everyone from far and wide to his castle. He started things off by calling Daniel a son-of-a-bitch. Thus scoring one point for royalty. They pulled each other's dick back and forth until Daniel said, "Speaking of whores, where is the queen?" Thus scoring one point for the common man.

The king ordered Daniel into the lion's pit. While Daniel was making friends with the lions, the courtiers out in the courtyard were slinging camel shit—for bullshit was as yet not invented in those days.

The king ordered Daniel forth. But Daniel slipped on some lion's shit and came in fifth.

"Where is the princess?" Daniel demanded.

"Fuck the princess," roared the king.

So Daniel and forty others got killed in the rush.

A Camelot Variation

Twas the night of the king's castration, 'twas the night of the king's last ball. All the counts and no-accounts were gathered in the hall, when in walked Sir Galahad with his left nut slung over his right shoulder.

"It tickles," said Sir Galahad.

"What tickles?" asked the King.

"Test-tickles," said Sir Galahad.

"Where's the Queen?" asked Sir Galahad.

"In bed with laryngitis," answered the King.

"Is that damn Greek here again?" asked Sir Galahad.

"Ah, fuck the Queen," roared the King.

Forty royal knights were trampled in the rush, for in those days the King's word was law.

BLINDED BY SHIT

Tune: "Villikens and His Dinah," or "Sweet Betsy from Pike"

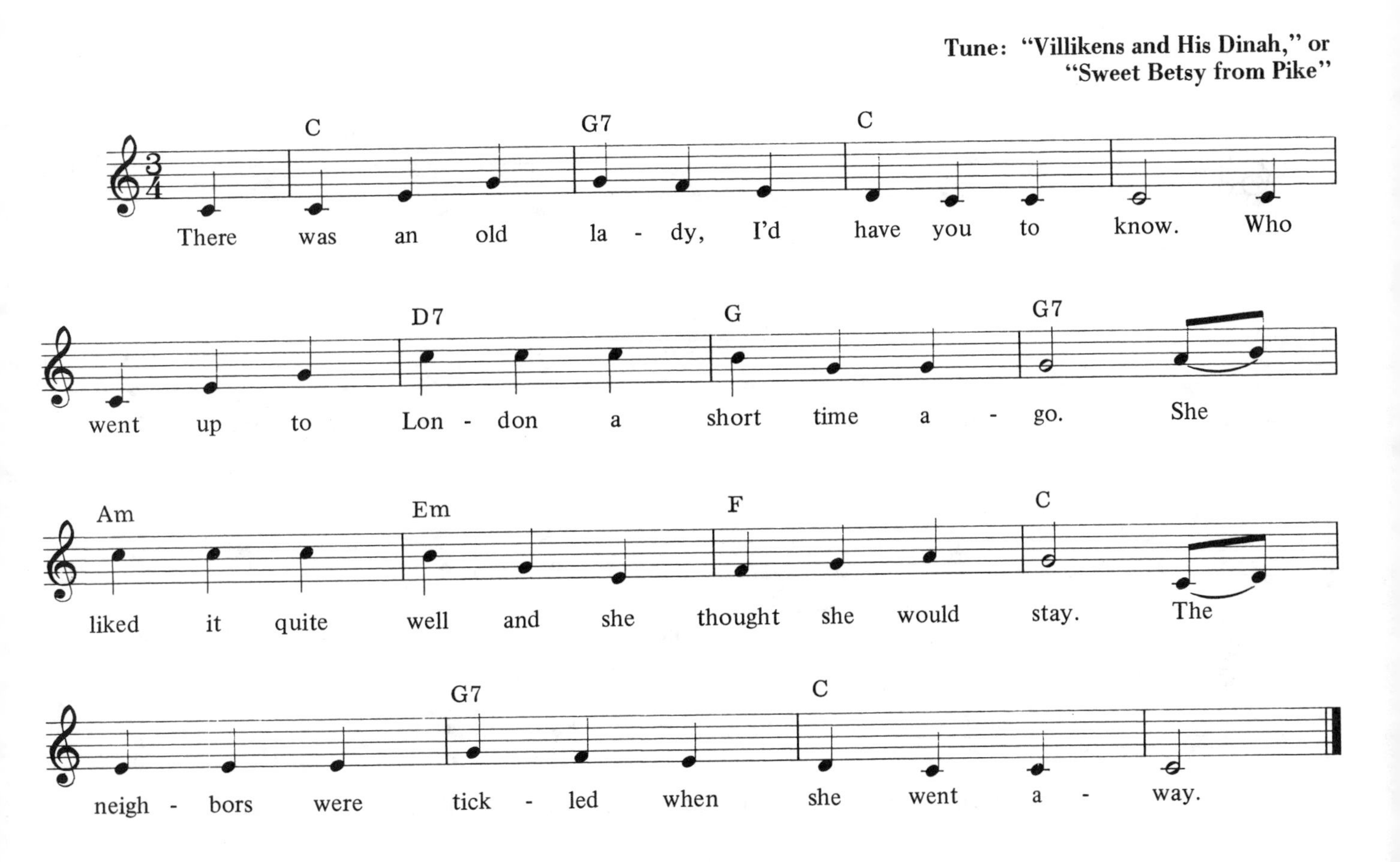
C G7 C
There was an old la - dy, I'd have you to know. Who
D7 G G7
went up to Lon - don a short time a - go. She
Am Em F C
liked it quite well and she thought she would stay. The
G7 C
neigh - bors were tick - led when she went a - way.

C G7
Now when this old lady
C
Retired for the night,
D7
She said, "Oh, gor blimey
G G7
I believe I must shite."
Am Em
There's no use in talking
F C
About things that have past.
G7
So up went the window
C
And out went her ass.

C G7
There was an old watchman
C
Who chanced to pass by,
D7
Looked up, got a chunk of shit
G G7
Right in the eye.
Am Em
He put up his hand
F C
To see where he was hit.
G7
He says, "Oh, gor blimey,
C
I'm blinded with shit."

C G7
Now this poor watchman
C
Was blinded for life.
D7
He had five healthy children
G G7
And a fine fucking wife.
Am Em
On a London street corner
F
You may now see him sit
G7
With a sign on his chest
C
Reading, "Blinded by shit."

THE BONNIEST LASS

By **ROBERT BURNS**

C Dm
The bon - ni - est lass that ye meet neist, Gie her a kiss an'
F C
a' that. In spite o' - il - ka par - ish priest, Re -
E7 Am C
pent - in' stool, an' a' that. For a' that an'
Dm
a: that, their mim - mou'd songs an' a' that, In
F C Am Dm E7 Am
time and place con - ve - ni - ent, They'll do't them-selves for a' that.

```
        C
Your patriarchs in days o' yore,
      Dm
Had their handmaids and a' that;
     F                C
O' bastard gets, some had a score,
       E7              Am
And some had mair than a' that.

           C
    For a' that an' a' that,
           Dm
    Your lansyne saunts, an' a' that
           F         C      Am
    Were fonder o' a bonnie lass,
           Dm   E7    Am
    Than you or I, for a' that.
```

C
King Davie, when he waxed auld,
Dm
An's bluid ran thin, an a' that,
F C
An' fand his cods were growin' cauld,
E7 Am
Could not refrain, for a' that.

C
For a' that an' a' that,
Dm
To keep him warm, an' a' that,
F C Am
The daughters o' Jerusalem
Dm E7 Am
Were waled for him, an a' that.

C
Wha wadna pity thae sweet dames
Dm
He fumbled at, an' a' that,
F C
An' raised their bluid up into flames
E7 Am
He couldna drown, for a' that.

C
For a' that an' a' that,
Dm
He wanted pith, an' a' that
F C Am
For, as to what we shall not name,
Dm E7 Am
What could he do but claw that.

C
King Solomon, prince o' divines,
Dm
Wha proverbs made, an' a' that,
F C
Baith mistresses and concubines
E7 Am
In hundreds had, for a' that.

C
For a' that an a' that,
Dm
Tho' a preacher wise an' a' that,
F C Am
The smuttiest sang that e'er was sung
Dm E7 Am
His Sang o' Sangs is a' that.

C
Then still I swear, a clever chiel
Dm
Should kiss a lass, an' a' that,
F C
Tho' priests consign him to the deil,
E7 Am
As reprobate, an' a' that.

C
For a' that an' a' that,
Dm
Their canting stuff, an' a' that,
F C Am
They ken nae mair what's reprobate
Dm E7 Am
Than you or I, for a' that.

Glossary

neist	next
ilka	every
mim-mou'd	mealy-mouthed
lansyne saunts	old-time saints
waled	picked
pith	strength
chiel	young fellow
deil	devil
ken nae mair	know no more

THE BRITISH GRENADIER

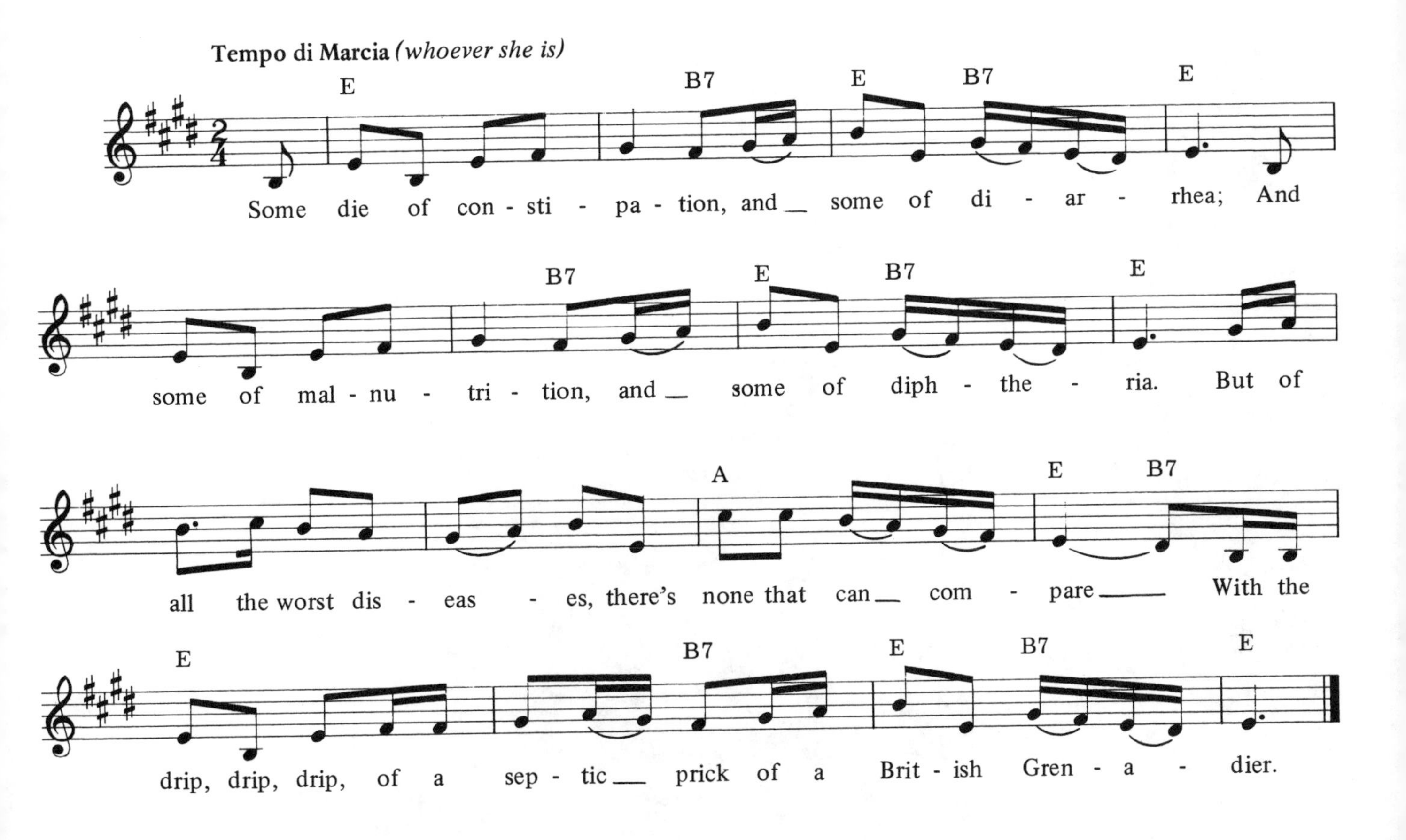
Tempo di Marcia *(whoever she is)*
E B7 E B7 E
Some die of con - sti - pa - tion, and __ some of di - ar - rhea; And
B7 E B7 E
some of mal - nu - tri - tion, and __ some of diph - the - ria. But of
A E B7
all the worst dis - eas - es, there's none that can __ com - pare ____ With the
E B7 E B7 E
drip, drip, drip, of a sep - tic __ prick of a Brit - ish Gren - a - dier.

E B7
When he goes forth in battle,
E B7
His weapon in his hand,
B7
The lasses fall like cattle,
E B7 E
There's none can make a stand.

But when the campaign's over,
A E B7
It's then he feels so queer:
E B7
With the drip, drip, drip of a septic prick
E B7 E
Of a British Grenadier.

E B7
And when he does retire,
E B7 E
To take his well-earned rest,
B7
There burns that ancient fire,
E B7 E
To do what he does best.

And yet, the truth is bitter –
A E B7
There's one thing he does fear:
E B7
It's the drip, drip, drip of a septic prick
E B7 E
Of a British Grenadier.

CATS ON THE ROOFTOPS

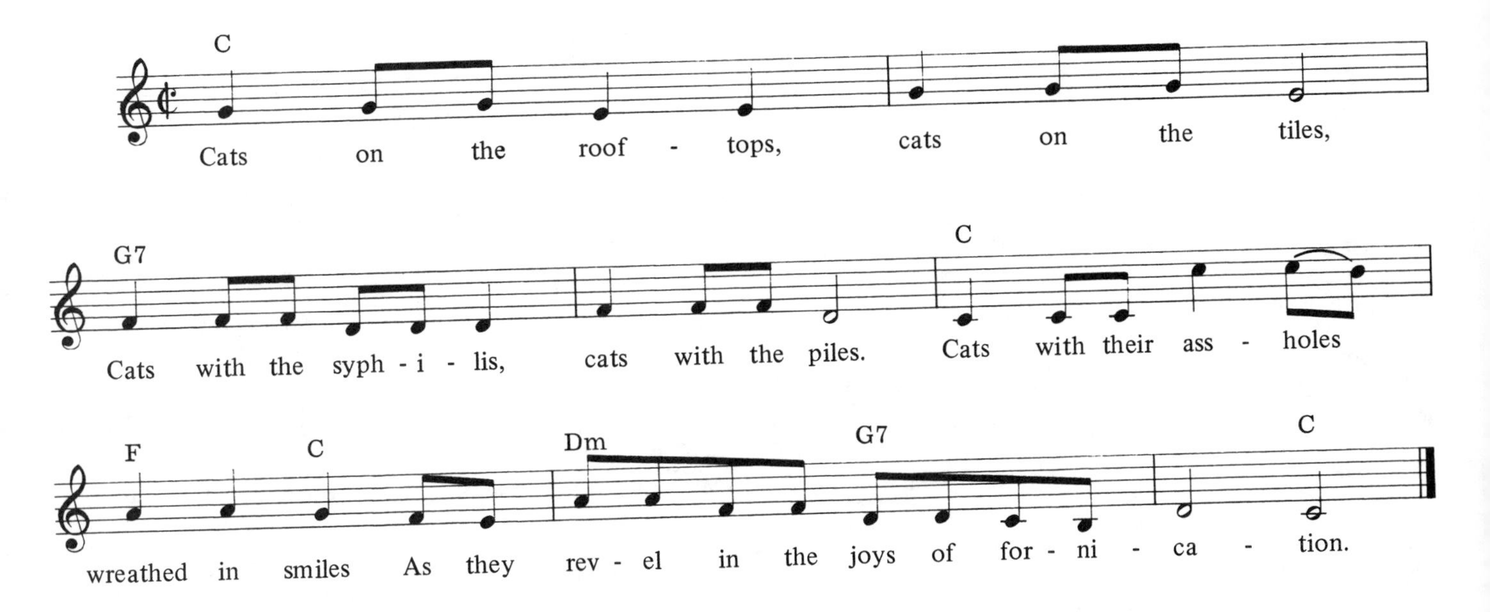
C
Cats on the roof - tops, cats on the tiles,
G7
Cats with the syph - i - lis, cats with the piles.
C
Cats with their ass - holes
F C Dm G7 C
wreathed in smiles As they rev - el in the joys of for - ni - ca - tion.

C
The monkey is a lively chap,
G7
He's known to take a flying crap.
C F C
And now and then he's clipped by clap,
Dm G7 C
As he revels in the joys of fornication.

C
The snag-tooth walrus is a beast
G7
Of whom we know the very least.
C F C
But when he fucks – great Judas Priest!
Dm G7 C
How he revels in the joys of fornication.

C
The hippo knows the latest style,
G7
And does his lady friends beguile.
C F C
And when he comes he floods the Nile,
Dm G7 C
As he revels in the joys of fornication.

C
The eagles they fly very high,
G7
And often shit right in our eye.
C F C
How glad I am that cows don't fly,
Dm G7 C
As we revel in the joys of fornication.

C
The cow is rather meek and kind,
G7
The calmest of all beasts, you'll find.
C F C
But when the bull mounts from behind,
Dm G7 C
How she revels in the joys of fornication.

C
The porcupine is full of quills,
G7
Which do protect it from all ills.
C F C
But I'm sure they must enhance the thrills
Dm G7 C
As it revels in the joys of fornication.

CHARLOTTE THE HARLOT

Tune: "Villikens and His Dinah," or "Sweet Betsy from Pike"

C G7 C
Down in cunt val - ley where giz - zum does flow, The
D7 G G7 Am
cock - suck - ers work for a dol - lar a blow. There lived pret - ty
Em F C G7
Char - lotte, the girl I a - dore, My__ free - fuck - ing, cock - suck - ing
C
cow - punch - er's whore.
Chorus:
Em F
Char - lotte, the har - lot, the girl I a -
C G7 C
dore. The__ pride of the prai - rie, the cow - punch - er's whore.

C G7 C
She's easy, she's greasy, she works on the street,
D7 G G7
And whenever you see her, she's always in heat.
Am Em F C
She'll do it for a dollar, take less or take more,
G7 C
She's Charlotte the harlot, the cowpunchers' whore. *Chorus*

C G7 C
One day on the prairie, while riding along,
D7 G G7
My seat in the saddle, the reins on my dong,
Am Em F
Who should I meet but the girl I adore,
G7 C
Charlotte the harlot, the cowpunchers' whore. *Chorus*

C G7 C
One day on the prairie, no pants on her quim,
D7 G G7
A rattlesnake saw her and slipped right on in.
Am Em F C
She wiggled, she giggled; it tickled down there.
G7 C
She had a vagina with rattles and hair. *Chorus*

C G7 C
I got off my pony, I reached for her crack.
D7 G G7
The damn thing was rattling and biting me back.
Am Em F C
I took out my pistol; I aimed for its head.
G7 C
I missed the damn rattler; I shot her instead. *Chorus*

C G7 C
Her funeral procession was forty miles long,
D7 G G7
With a chorus of cowpunchers singing this song:
Am Em F
"Here lies a young maiden who'll screw us no more,
G7 C
Young Charlotte the harlot, the cowpunchers' whore." *Chorus*

THE CHINATOWN BUMBOAT

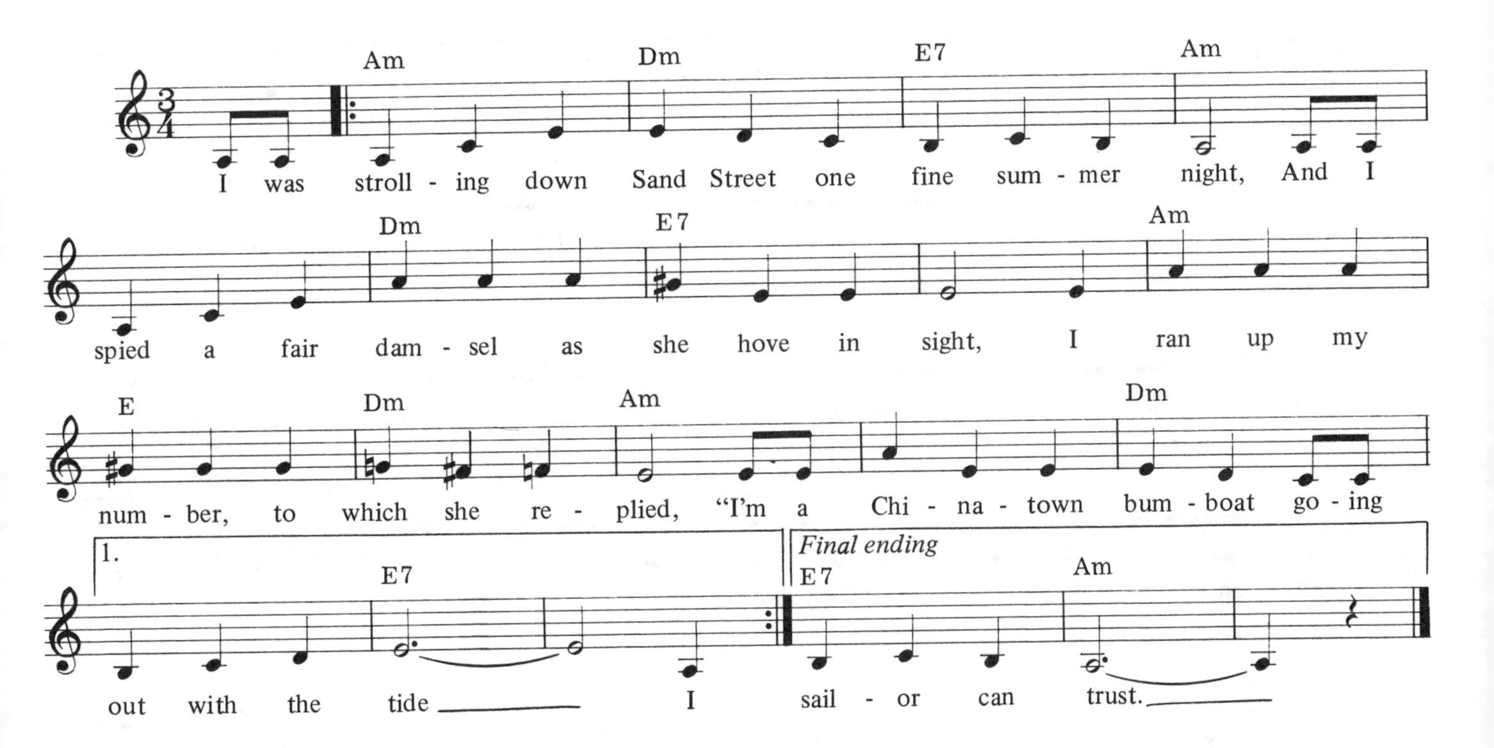
Am Dm E7 Am
I was stroll - ing down Sand Street one fine sum - mer night, And I
Dm E7 Am
spied a fair dam - sel as she hove in sight, I ran up my
E Dm Am Dm
num - ber, to which she re - plied, "I'm a Chi - na - town bum - boat go - ing
1.
E7
out with the tide I
Final ending
E7 Am
sail - or can trust.

Am Dm E7 Am
I throwed out a hawser and took her tow,
Dm E7
We crossed down the way like a couple should go.
Am E Dm Am
We turned in an alley not too clean or neat,
Dm E7
We dropped our mudhooks at the end of the street.

Am Dm E7 Am
She then led me up to a third-story floor,
Dm E7
And in her fine stateroom I soon laid her o'er.
Am E Dm Am
She cleaned up her courses and her red flag downhaul,
Dm E7
She laid her white hand on my boat-tackle fall.

Am Dm E7 Am
I gazed in her sternsheets and saw plenty of room,
Dm E7
And into her hull-pipe I stowed my jib boom
Am E Dm Am
With her fenders o'erhanging like a bent scupper's lip,
Dm E7
Pretty Polly's a pirate that scuttled me ship.

Am Dm E7 Am
She rolled and she pitched like a ship in a storm,
Dm E7
She cried out, "Oh sailor, you're doing me harm.
Am E Dm Am
You're in the wrong port!" she cried out in alarm.
Dm E7
Well, the wrong port be damned – any port in a storm.

Am Dm E7 Am
She burnt down me rigging clean down to the hull,
Dm E7
So back to the sickbay me punt I did scull.
Am E Dm Am
With my foregaps all bent and my mainmast unstrung,
Dm E7
The doctor says, "Sailor, your jib boom is sprung."

Am Dm E7 Am
I'm lying in the sickbay, my stern to the wall,
Dm E7
The Chinatown bumboat the cause of it all.
Am E Dm Am
It's ashes to ashes and dust unto dust,
Dm E7 Am
Just show me the woman a sailor can trust.

CHRISTOPHER COLUMBO

Verse:
D
A7
In four-teen hun-dred nine-ty-two, A sail-or from It-a-ly, He
D
walked the dirt-y streets of Spain and shat in ev-'ry al-ley. At
A7
that time reigned a fair young Queen of Spain, named Is-a-bel-la, Who
D
Chorus:
cast an am-or-osh-us glance at Chris, the smart young fel-la. He
D
A7
D
knew the world was round, oh, His balls did touch the ground, oh. That
A7
D
A7
D
syph-i-lit-ic, hyp-o-crit-ic, son-of-a-bitch Co-lum-bo.
D
Columbo went to the Queen of Spain
A7
And made a proposition.
But what she wanted most to do
D
Was fuck in the prone position.
The Queen of Spain then said to him
A7
She'd give him ships and cargo.
He said, "I'll kiss your royal ass
D
If I don't bring back Chicago."
D
A7
Chorus: He knew the world was round, oh.
D
The queenly cunt he'd pound, oh.
A7
D
That fornicating, royal-mating,
A7
D
Son-of-a-bitch, Columbo.
D
Three little ships set out to sea,
A7
Each one a double-decker.
The queen she waved the royal flag,
D
Columbo waved his pecker.
Columbo paced upon the deck,
A7
He knew it was his duty.
He took his whang into his hand
D
And said, "Ain't that a beauty!"
D
A7
Chorus: He knew the world was round, oh.
D
That sailors could be browned, oh.
A7
D
That dirty lecher, ass-hole stretcher,
A7
D
Son-of-a-bitch, Columbo.

D
Columbus had a second mate
A7
He loved just like a brother,

And every night below the decks
D
They bung-holed one another.

The fourteen-year-old cabin boy,
A7
That dirty little nipper,

Shoved powdered glass right up his ass
D
And circumcised the skipper.

D A7
Chorus: He knew the world was round, oh.
D
His pecker it was ground, oh.
A7 D
That bleeding fucker, weenie-sucker,
A7 D
Son-of-a-bitch, Columbo.

D
For forty days and forty nights
A7
They sailed the broad Atlantic,

That till at last for a piece of ass
D
The whole crew it grew frantic.

A mermaid came a-swimming by,
A7
The crew let out a holler,

And when they tossed her back to sea
D
She'd made ten thousand dollars.

D A7
Chorus: He knew the world was round, oh.
D
That tail-o could be found, oh.
A7 D
That navigating, masturbating,
A7 D
Son-of-a-bitch, Columbo.

D
An Indian maid appeared on shore,
A7
Columbo soon pursued her.

The white of an egg rolled down her leg,
D
The son-of-a-bitch, he screwed her.

And when he got back home to Spain
A7
To tell of his adventures,

Queen Isabella sucked him off,
D
Of course, without her dentures.

D A7
Final Chorus: He knew the world was round, oh.
D
His dangling dong was crowned, oh.
A7 D
That syphilitic, hypocritic,
A7 D
Fornicating, royal-mating,
A7 D
Dirty lecher, ass-hole stretcher,
A7 D
Bleeding fucker, weenie-sucker,
A7 D
Navigating, masturbating,
A7 D
SON-OF-A-BITCH, COLUMBO!

Sing measure 3 of chorus five times

Les douze Signes –
les 6. p^er. marque^t. le Cocuage
le Cerf
la Licorne
le Belier
le Taureau
le Bouc
le Limaçon

COMIN' THRO' THE RYE

By **ROBERT BURNS**

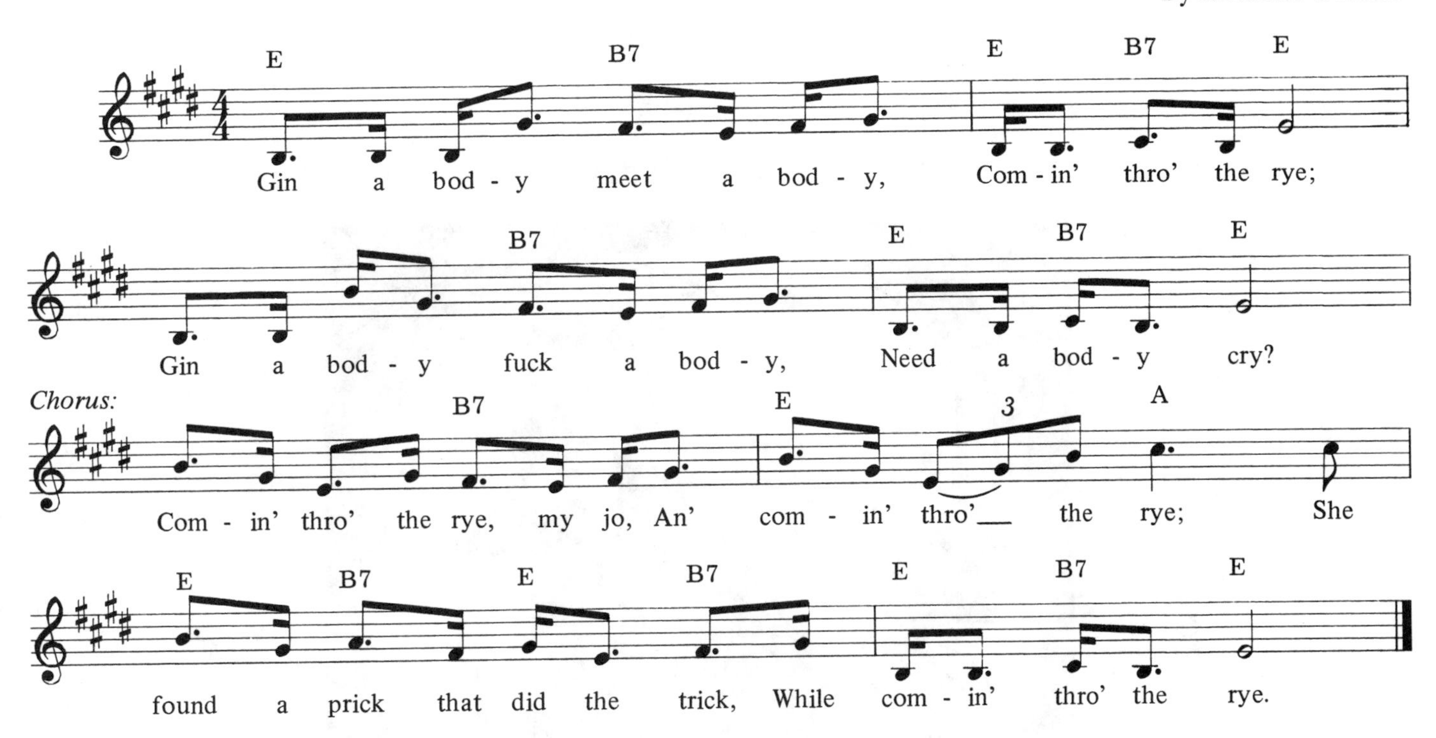
E B7 E B7 E
Gin a bod - y meet a bod - y, Com - in' thro' the rye;
B7 E B7 E
Gin a bod - y fuck a bod - y, Need a bod - y cry?
Chorus:
B7 E 3 A
Com - in' thro' the rye, my jo, An' com - in' thro' the rye; She
E B7 E B7 E B7 E
found a prick that did the trick, While com - in' thro' the rye.

E B7
Gin a body meet a body,
E B7 E
Comin' thro' the glen;
B7
Gin a body fuck a body,
E B7 E
Need the warld ken. *Chorus*

E B7
Gin a body meet a body,
E B7 E
Comin' thro' the grain;
B7
Gin a body fuck a body,
E B7 E
Cunt's a body's ain. *Chorus*

E B7
Gin a body meet a body,
E B7 E
By a body's sel,
B7
What na body fucks a body,
E B7 E
Wad a body tell. *Chorus*

E B7
Mony a body meets a body,
E B7 E
They dare na weel avow;
B7
Mony a body fucks a body,
E B7 E
Ye wadna think it true. *Chorus*

CROCK OF SHIT

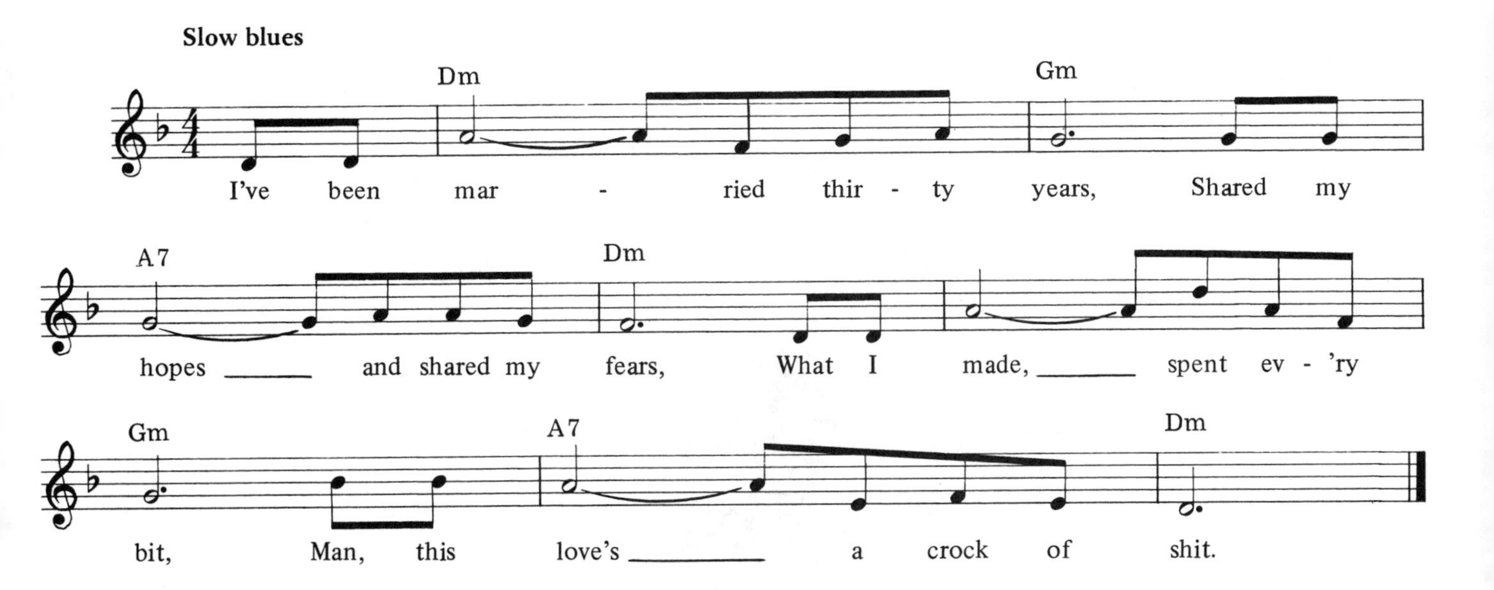
Slow blues
Dm
Gm
I've been mar - ried thir - ty years, Shared my
A7
Dm
hopes ___ and shared my fears, What I made, ___ spent ev - 'ry
Gm
A7
Dm
bit, Man, this love's ___ a crock of shit.

```
Dm                 Gm
I sent all my kids to school,
          A7              Dm
Now they think that I'm a fool.
                               Gm
They don't like me 'cause I spit:
        A7               Dm
Man, this love's a crock of shit.

     Dm                 Gm
After work most every night,
        A7             Dm
I came home – we had a fight.
                      Gm
My wife always was a wit;
        A7              Dm
Man, this love's a crock of shit.

     Dm              Gm
If you haven't yet got wed,
        A7             Dm
Listen close to what I've said.
                                Gm
Freedom's still within your mitt;
        A7              Dm
Man, this love's a crock of shit.
```

DAISY, DAISY

G C G
Dais - y, Dais - y, give me your an - swer true,
D7 G Em A7 D
Dais - y, Dais - y, would - n't you like to screw? I
D7 G
real - ly must beg your par - don, But I've got a
C G D7 G D7
hell of a hard on, From beat - ing my meat a -
G D7 G D7 G
gainst the seat of a bi - cy - cle built for two.

THE DARBY RAM

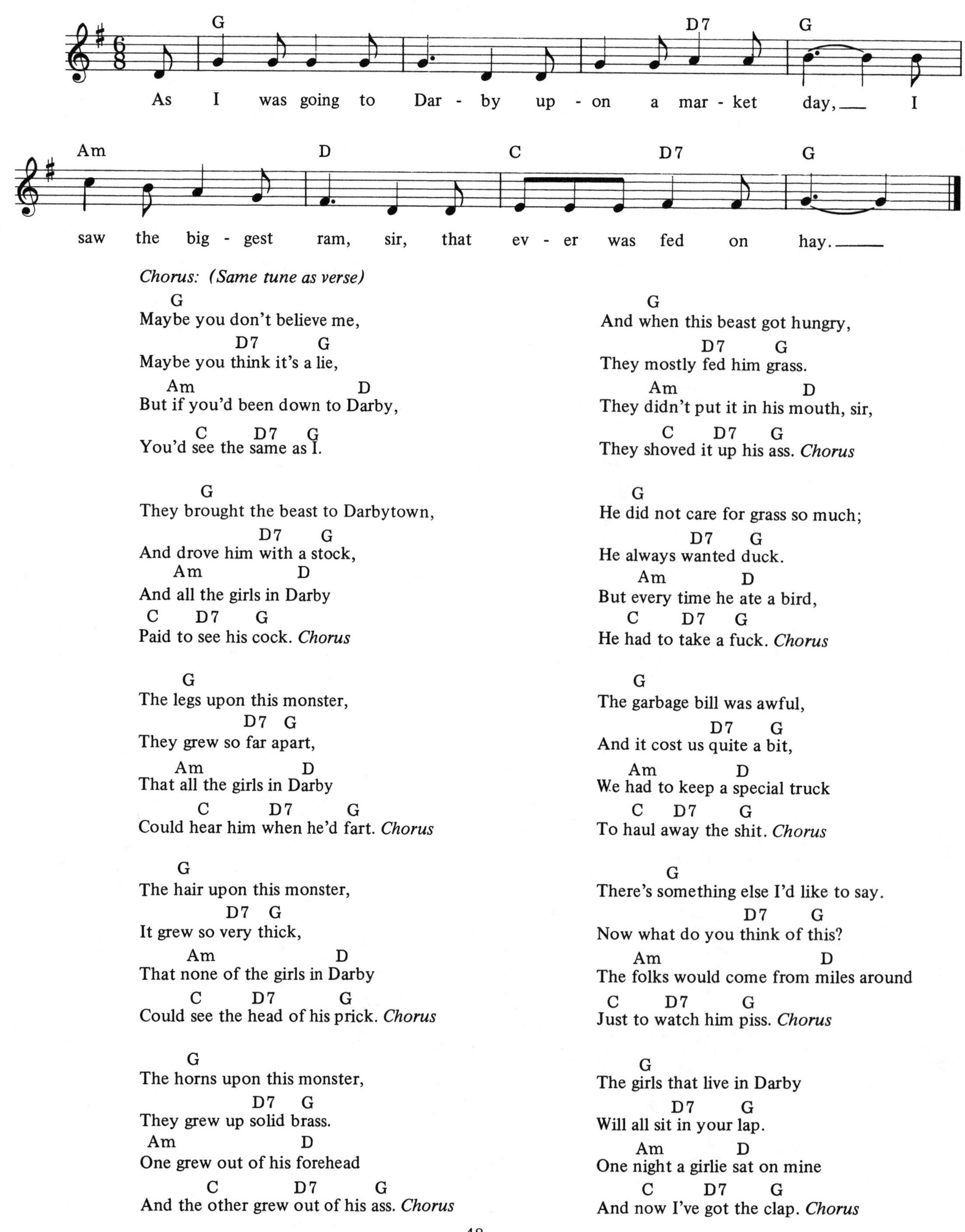
G D7 G
As I was going to Dar - by up - on a mar - ket day, I
Am D C D7 G
saw the big - gest ram, sir, that ev - er was fed on hay.
Chorus: (Same tune as verse)
G
Maybe you don't believe me,
D7 G
Maybe you think it's a lie,
Am D
But if you'd been down to Darby,
C D7 G
You'd see the same as I.
G
They brought the beast to Darbytown,
D7 G
And drove him with a stock,
Am D
And all the girls in Darby
C D7 G
Paid to see his cock. Chorus
G
The legs upon this monster,
D7 G
They grew so far apart,
Am D
That all the girls in Darby
C D7 G
Could hear him when he'd fart. Chorus
G
The hair upon this monster,
D7 G
It grew so very thick,
Am D
That none of the girls in Darby
C D7 G
Could see the head of his prick. Chorus
G
The horns upon this monster,
D7 G
They grew up solid brass.
Am D
One grew out of his forehead
C D7 G
And the other grew out of his ass. Chorus
G
And when this beast got hungry,
D7 G
They mostly fed him grass.
Am D
They didn't put it in his mouth, sir,
C D7 G
They shoved it up his ass. Chorus
G
He did not care for grass so much;
D7 G
He always wanted duck.
Am D
But every time he ate a bird,
C D7 G
He had to take a fuck. Chorus
G
The garbage bill was awful,
D7 G
And it cost us quite a bit,
Am D
We had to keep a special truck
C D7 G
To haul away the shit. Chorus
G
There's something else I'd like to say.
D7 G
Now what do you think of this?
Am D
The folks would come from miles around
C D7 G
Just to watch him piss. Chorus
G
The girls that live in Darby
D7 G
Will all sit in your lap.
Am D
One night a girlie sat on mine
C D7 G
And now I've got the clap. Chorus

DINAH

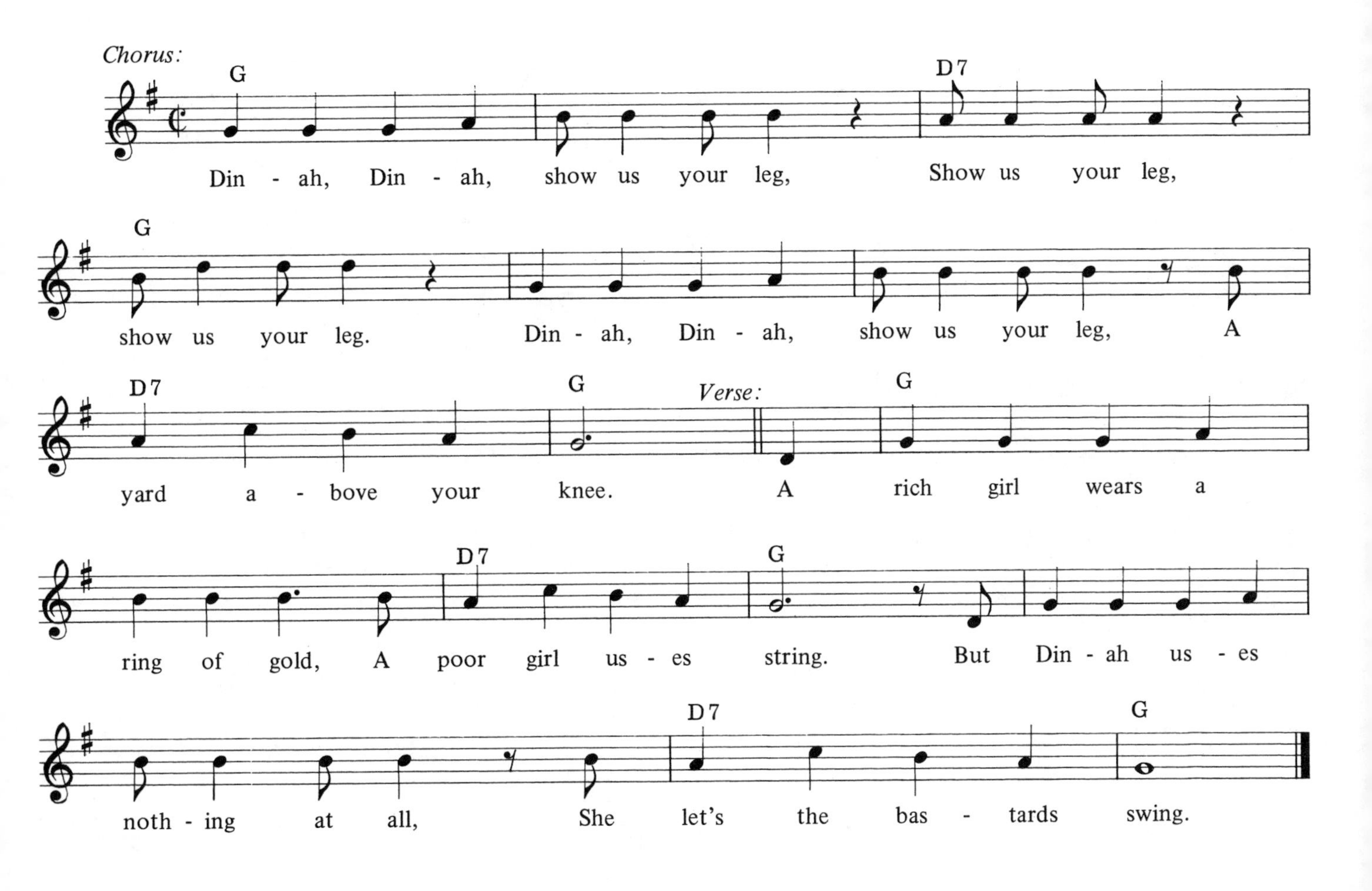
Chorus:
G
D7
Din - ah, Din - ah, show us your leg, Show us your leg,
G
show us your leg. Din - ah, Din - ah, show us your leg, A
D7
G
Verse:
G
yard a - bove your knee. A rich girl wears a
D7
G
ring of gold, A poor girl us - es string. But Din - ah us - es
D7
G
noth - ing at all, She let's the bas - tards swing.

```
G
A rich girl wears a ring of gold,
 D7              G
A poor girl, one of brass.

But the only ring that Dinah's got
     D7              G
Is the one around her ass. Chorus
```

```
    G
A rich girl drives a limousine,
 D7              G
A poor girl drives a truck.

But the only ride that Dinah has
     D7              G
Is when she has a fuck. Chorus
```

```
    G
A rich girl uses vaseline,
 D7              G
A poor girl uses lard.

But Dinah uses axle grease
     D7                 G
Because her cunt's so hard. Chorus
```

DON'T CRY, LADY

Chorus:
C
Don't cry, la - dy, I'll buy your God - damn' vio - lets, Don't cry
D7 G7 C C7 F
la - dy, Your pen - cils, too. Don't cry la - dy, Take off those
D7 C E7 Am D7 G7 C
Fine
col - ored glass - es. Hel - lo, moth - er, I knew it was you.
Verse:
C
Hoo - ray, hoo - ray, my fa - ther's gon - na get shot. Hoo - ray, hoo -
G7 C C7
ray, that dir - ty, drunk-en sot, For he was ver - y mean to me when
F F♯dim C Am D7 G7 C G7
D. C. al Fine
I was just a tot, Hoo - ray, they're gon - na shoot my fa - ther, So

C
Hooray, hooray, my uncle's gonna get hung.
G7
Hooray, hooray, that dirty drunken bum;
C C7 F F♯dim
For he was very mean to me when I was very young –
C Am D7 G7 C G7
Hooray, they're gonna hang my un - cle. So, *Chorus*

C
Hooray, hooray, my brother's gonna get hurt.
G7
Hooray, hooray, that dirty sex pervert;
C C7 F F♯dim
For he was very free with me when I was just a squirt –
C Am D7 G7 C G7
Hooray, they're gonna hurt my broth - er. So, *Chorus*

C
Hooray, hooray, my cousin's gonna get destroyed.
G7
Hooray, hooray, that no good anthropoid;
C C7 F F♯dim
For he would always try on me the things he'd read in Freud –
C Am D7 G7 C G7
Hooray, they're gonna wreck my cous - in. So, *Chorus*

DO YOUR BALLS HANG LOW?

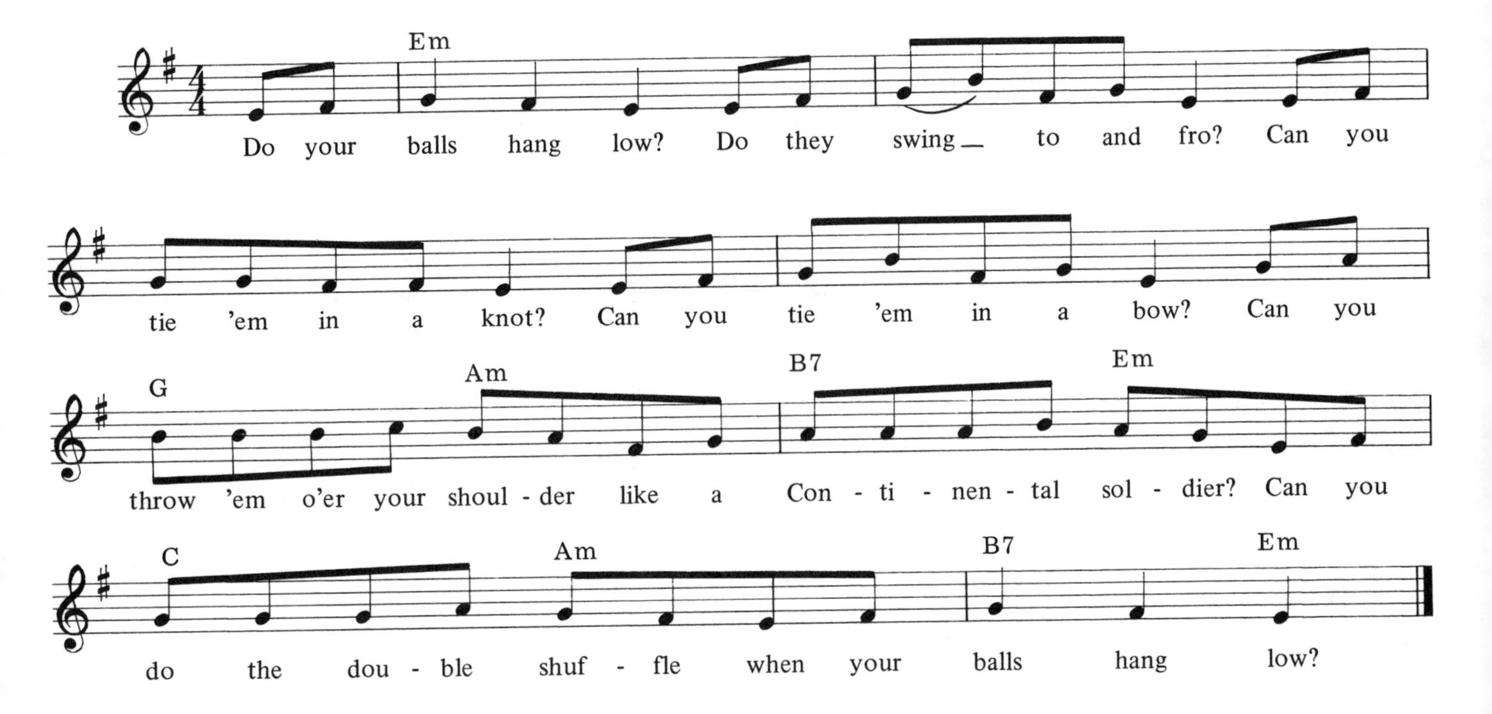
Em
Do your balls hang low? Do they swing — to and fro? Can you
tie 'em in a knot? Can you tie 'em in a bow? Can you
G Am B7 Em
throw 'em o'er your shoul - der like a Con - ti - nen - tal sol - dier? Can you
C Am B7 Em
do the dou - ble shuf - fle when your balls hang low?

Chorus: (Same tune as verse)

Em
Ting-a-ling, God damn, find a woman if you can.

If you can't find a woman, find a clean old man.
G Am B7 Em
If you're ever in Gibraltar, take a flying fuck at Walter.
C Am B7 Em
Can you do the double shuffle when your balls hang low?

Additional lyrics for measures 5 and 6:

G Am B7 Em
Do they make a lusty clamor when you hit them with a hammer?
G Am B7 Em
Can you bounce 'em off the wall like an Indian rubber ball?
G Am B7 Em
Do they have a hollow sound when you drag 'em on the ground?
G Am B7 Em
Do they have a mellow tingle when you hit 'em with a shingle?
G Am B7 Em
Do they have a salty taste when you wrap 'em 'round your waist?
G Am B7 E
Do they chime like a gong when you pull upon your dong?

DRIVE IT HOME

E
B7
I gave her in - ches one, drive it home, drive it home. I
E
gave her in - ches one, drive it home, drive it home. I
E7
A
gave her in - ches one, She said, "John - ny, this is fun. Put your
B7
E A E
bel - ly close to mine and drive it home, drive it home."

I gave her inches two, drive it home, drive it home.
I gave her inches two, drive it home, drive it home.
I gave her inches two,
She said, "Johnny, this won't do.
Put your belly close to mine and drive it home, drive it home."

...inches three...this is free...

...inches four...let's have an encore...

...inches five...it's alive...

...inches six...show me all your tricks...

...inches seven...this is heaven...

...inches eight...this is great...

...inches nine...it's all mine...

...inches ten...let's do it again...

While we are on the subject, the following two-part graffito observed in a New York City subway station seems appropriate:

I am 9 inches long and 4 inches around. Interested?
Yes, how big is your cock?

THE EAGLES, THEY FLY HIGH

E B7
Oh, the ea - gles, they fly high o - ver Mo - bile,
E
Oh, the ea - gles, they fly high o - ver Mo - bile,
A E
Oh, the ea - gles, they fly high and they shit right in your
B7 E
eye. Oh I'm glad that cows don't fly o - ver Mo - bile.

E B7
Oh, the boys way up at Yale get no tail,

Oh, the boys way up at Yale get no tail.
A
From a lack of recreation
E
They resort to masturbation –
B7 E
It's a helluva situation up at Yale.

Speaking (or singing) of the ivy-covered walls of academe, who can forget the classic

> High above Cayuga's waters, there's an awful smell,
> Where ten thousand sons of bitches call themselves Cornell.

Or the succinct

> What's the color of horseshit?
> Brown! Brown! Brown!

This New York City subway graffito makes a similar point, rather crudely for my taste:

> Fuck all boys from Princeton

EMPTY BED BLUES

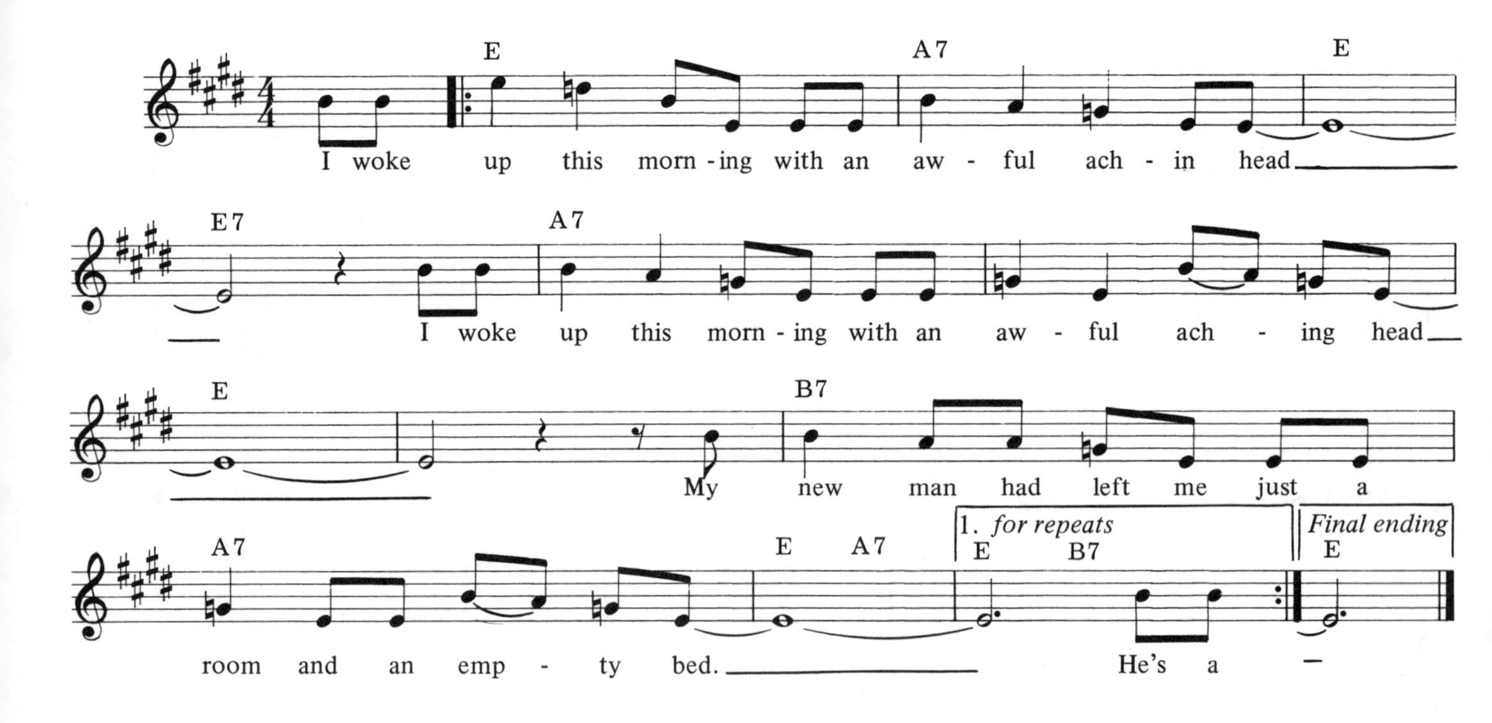
E
A7
E
I woke up this morn - ing with an aw - ful ach - in head
E7
A7
I woke up this morn - ing with an aw - ful ach - ing head
E
B7
My new man had left me just a
A7
E A7
1. for repeats
E B7
Final ending
E
room and an emp - ty bed.
He's a

E A7 E E7
He's a coffee grinder – grinding all the time,
A7 E
He's a coffee grinder – grinding all the time,
B7 A7 E A7 E B7
He can grind my coffee, 'cause he's got a brand-new grind.

E A7 E E7
He's a deep-sea diver with a stroke that can't go wrong,
A7 E
He's a deep-sea diver with a stroke that can't go wrong,
B7 A7 E A7 E B7
He can reach the bottom 'cause his breath holds out so long.

E A7 E E7
He came home one evening with his spirit 'way up high,
A7 E
He came home one evening with his spirit 'way up high,
B7 A7 E A7 E B7
What he had to give me made me wring my hands and cry.

E A7 E E7
He taught me a lesson I never had before,
A7 E
He taught me a lesson I never had before,
B7 A7 E A7 E B7
When he got through teaching, from my elbows down I was sore.

```
          E                         A7          E  E7
Well, he boiled my cabbage and he made it awful hot,
         A7                                    E
Well, he boiled my cabbage and he made it awful hot,
          B7              A7               E A7  E   B7
Then he put in the bacon and overflowed the pot.

           E                         A7                E   E7
Well, he knows how to thrill me, and I told my girl friend, Lou,
           A7                                          E
Well, he knows how to thrill me, and I told my girl friend, Lou,
          B7                          A7               E   A7   E    B7
And the way she's raving she must have gone and tried it too.

        E                 A7                 E   E7
If you get good loving, never go and spread the news,
      A7                                    E
If you get good loving, never go and spread the news,
            B7          A7                               E  A7   E
Gals will doublecross you and leave you with the Empty Bed Blues.
```

ESKIMO NELL

G D7
Don't look at me that way, strang - er, My pants ain't
G
full of shit, It's just this God damned
D A7 D D7
syph - il - lis, Eat - ing me bit by bit. When a
G D7
man grows old and his balls get cold, And the end of his
G C C♯dim
knob goes blue, And it sags in the mid - dle like a
G E7 A7 D7 G
one - string fid - dle, He can tell a tale or two.

G D7
So, drag up your chairs and buy me a drink,
G
And a tale to you I'll tell
D
About Deadeye Dick and Mexican Pete,
A7 D D7
And a gal named Eskimo Nell.
G D7
Now, Deadeye Dick and Mexican Pete
G
Arrived at about high noon,
C C♯dim G E7
And each man on his horse rode straight, of course,
A7 D7 G
For the Rio Grande Saloon.

G D7
The swing-doors crashed against weathered walls,
G
Both prick and gun flashed free.
D
"According to sex, you pox-ridden wrecks,
A7 D D7
You drink or fuck with me."
G D7
Now the men down there had heard of Pete,
G
North of the Panama,
C C♯dim G E7
So with nothing worse than a muttered curse,
A7 D7 G
They headed for the bar.

G D7
The women, too, had heard of Dick,
G
Down on the Rio Grande,
D
So, forty whores took down their drawers,
A7 D D7
At Deadeye Dick's command.
G D7
Now, forty asses is a handsome sight,
G
To a man with a mighty stand,
C C♯dim G E7
It's mighty rare on Barclay Square,
A7 D7 G
But it's not on the Rio Grande.

G D7
Now, Deadeye Dick was breathing quick,
G
And panting in short grunts,
D
As forty asses were bared to view,
A7 D D7
To say nothing of forty cunts.
G D7
Dick backed to the door and the number one whore
G
Could see in the chandelier's prism
C C♯dim G E7
How he sprang through air — his ballocks all bare,
A7 D7 G
As he sprayed her with his gism.

G D7
He bore her to the sandy floor,
G
And he fucked her fair and fine,
D
And although she grinned she put the wind
A7 D D7
Up the other thirty nine.
G D7
Now, Deadeye Dick, he fucked them quick,
G
And he cast the first aside,
C C♯dim G E7
And he made a dart at the second tart,
A7 D7 G
When the doors flew open wide.

G D7
When into that deadly den of sin,
G
Yes, into that harlot's hell
D
There stepped a maid who was not afraid,
A7 D D7
Her name was Eskimo Nell.
G D7
Nell cried out loud above the crowd,
G
In accents clear and cool,
C C♯dim G E7
"You cunt-struck shrimp of a Yankee pimp,
A7 D7 G
Do you call that thing a tool?"

G D7
She took off her garments one by one,
G
With an air of modest pride,
D
And with subtle ease drew up her knees,
A7 D D7
And exposed the Great Divide.
G D7
She sat on a nearby table top,
G
Where someone had left a glass.
C C♯dim G E7
With a flick of her tits she ground it to bits
A7 D7 G
'Neath the cheeks of her dainty ass.

G D7
Now, Deadeye Dick he knew a trick
G
Or two so he took his time.
D
A dame like this was fucking bliss,
A7 D D7
So he played the pantomime.
G D7
From all his years of fucking queers,
G
He knew that now this was it.
C C♯dim G E7
For her cunt gripped his cock like the patent lock
A7 D7 G
Of the National Safe Deposit.

(continued)

```
        G                   D7
Dick fell to the floor, he knew no more,
                            G
Both prick and face were red.
                                      D
Though he gave no shout when his cock came out,
      A7                      D         D7
It was fairly stripped of the thread.
        G                        D7
Then Pete jumped up with an angry scowl,
                         G
To avenge his friend's affront.
       C    C#dim   G        E7
And with a jolt he drew his Colt,
       A7      D7     G
And rammed it up her cunt.
```

```
                G                    D7
Now, he rammed it up to the trigger guard,
                                 G
And he fired it twice times three.
                       D
To his surprise she closed her eyes
        A7        D
With a sigh of ecstasy.
       G                          D7
Then Eskimo Nell said, "You've rung my bell,
                   G
I'm ready to explode.
        C       C#dim      G      E7
Oh Pete, my sweet, can you repeat."
      A7          D7         G
Said he, "I've shot my load."
```

```
        G               D7
So Deadeye Dick and Mexican Pete
                         G
Staggered out of the Rio Grande.
                           D
Deadeye Dick with his useless prick,
      A7                     D    D7
And Pete with no gun in his hand.
```

Moral:

```
       G                   D7
The folk of the frozen northland
                 G
Know how to copulate.
         C      C#dim     G      E7
Where even the dead lie two in a bed,
            A7   D7    G
And the babies masturbate.
```

FRIGGIN' IN THE RIGGIN'

Chorus:
C G7 C
Frig - gin' in the rig - gin', Frig - gin' in the rig - gin',
F G7 C
Frig - gin' in the rig - gin', There's fuck - all else to do.
Verse:
C G7
The cab - in boy was nip - per, He
C
was a dir - ty rip - per, He stuffed his ass with
F G7 C
bro - ken glass and cir - cum - cized the skip - per.

C G7
The Captain's daughter, Mabel,
C
Whenever she was able,
F
She took the crew for a midnight screw
G7 C
Upon the galley table. *Chorus*

C G7
While crossing the equator,
C
The crew did elevate her.
F
She bared her ass on the topmost mast,
G7 C
And dared us all to mate her. *Chorus*

C G7
Becalmed in the Sargasso,
C
To make the doldrums pass-o,
F
We launched a spree of buggery
G7 C
Upon each other's ass-o. *Chorus*

C G7
While sailing on the ocean,
C
We often have the notion,
F
In cold and heat, to beat the meat
G7 C
With a peculiar motion. *Chorus*

C G7
We knew sooner or later,
C
Approaching the equator,
F
That every Jack would have a whack
G7 C
At turning fornicator. *Chorus*

C G7
Each sailor lad's a brother
C
To all and one another.
F
We take great pains at our daisy chains,
G7 C
While writing home to mother. *Chorus*

THE FARTING CONTEST

Tune: "Villikens and His Dinah," or
"Sweet Betsy from Pike"

C Dm G7 C
I'll tell you a sto - ry that is sure to please, Of a great fart - ing
D7 G G7 Am Em
con - test at Sut - ton - on - Peas; Where all the best ars - es pa -
F C Dm G7 C
rad - ed the field, To com - pete in a con - test for var - i - ous shields.

C Dm G7 C
Some tighten their arses and fart up the scale,
D7 G G7
To compete for a cup and a barrel of ale.
Am Em F C
While others whose arses are biggest and strongest,
Dm G7 C
Compete in the section for loudest and longest.

C Dm G7 C
Now, this year's event had drawn quite a big crowd,
D7 G G7
And the betting was even on Mrs. McDowd.
Am Em F C
For it had appeared in the evening edition,
Dm G7 C
That this lady's arse was in perfect condition.

C Dm G7 C
Mrs. Bingle arrived amid roars of applause,
D7 G G7
And promptly proceeded to pull off her drawers.
Am Em F C
For though she'd no chance in the farting display,
Dm G7 C
She'd the prettiest bottom you'd see in a day.

C Dm G7 C
Now, young Mrs. Porter was backed for a place,
D7 G G7
Though she'd often been placed in the deepest disgrace
Am Em F C
By dropping a fart on a Sunday in church,
Dm G7 C
And disturbing the sermon of Reverend McGurch.

C Dm G7 C
The ladies lined up at the signal to start,
D7 G G7
And winning the toss, Mrs. Jones to first fart.
Am Em F C
The people around stood in silence and wonder,
Dm G7 C
While her wireless transmitted gale force and thunder.

C Dm G7 C
Now, Mrs. McDowd reckoned nothing of this,
D7 G G7
For she'd had some weak tea and was all wind and piss.
Am Em F C
So she took up her place and her arse opened wide,
Dm G7 C
But, unluckily shit and was disqualified.

```
           C            Dm            G7               C
Then young Mrs. Porter was called to the front,
                      D7           G             G7
And started by doing a wonderful stunt.
    Am               Em                F              C
She took a deep breath, and clenching her hands,
                              Dm                G7          C
She blew the damned roof off the popular stands.

         C           Dm             G7         C
This left Mrs. Bingle, who shyly appeared,
                           D7              G           G7
And smiled at the clergy, who lustily cheered.
       Am                  Em                   F                       C
And though it was thought that her chances were small,
                    Dm            G7             C
She ran out a winner, out-farting them all.

      C               Dm                G7         C
She went to the rostrum with dignified gait,
                        D7       G              G7
And took from the vicar a set of gold plate.
              Am               Em                  F           C
Then she turned to the clergy with sweetness sublime,
                           Dm              G7            C
And smiling, said, "Come up and see me sometime."

         C            Dm                  G7         C
The clergy was shocked by Miz Bingle's remark,
                         D7                  G                G7
Though some felt a stirring 'neath vestment and sark.
    Am                 Em               F                        C
Perhaps 'twas the wind – but who could have guessed?
                        Dm              G7         C
And that was the end of the farting contest.
```

Collected in Scotland by Dr. Rima Laibow

THE FINEST FUCKING FAMILY IN THE LAND

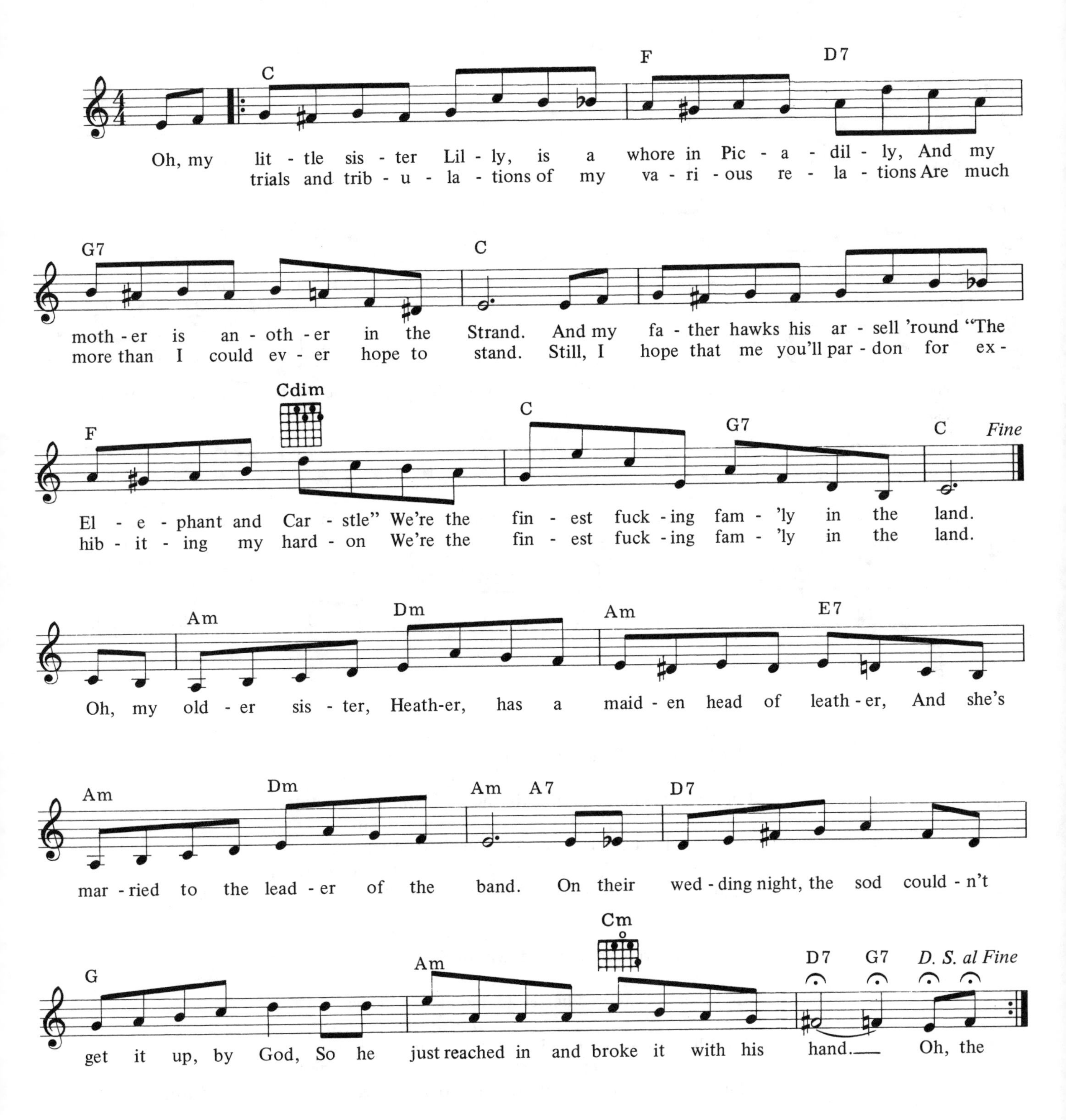
C F D7
Oh, my lit - tle sis - ter Lil - ly, is a whore in Pic - a - dil - ly, And my
trials and trib - u - la - tions of my va - ri - ous re - la - tions Are much
G7 C
moth - er is an - oth - er in the Strand. And my fa - ther hawks his ar - sell 'round "The
more than I could ev - er hope to stand. Still, I hope that me you'll par - don for ex -
F Cdim C G7 C Fine
El - e - phant and Car - stle" We're the fin - est fuck - ing fam - 'ly in the land.
hib - it - ing my hard - on We're the fin - est fuck - ing fam - 'ly in the land.
Am Dm Am E7
Oh, my old - er sis - ter, Heath-er, has a maid - en head of leath - er, And she's
Am Dm Am A7 D7
mar - ried to the lead - er of the band. On their wed - ding night, the sod could - n't
G Am Cm D7 G7 D. S. al Fine
get it up, by God, So he just reached in and broke it with his hand. Oh, the

THE FIRESHIP

G D7
As I walked out one ev - en - ing up - on my night's ca - reer I
G D7
spied a pret - ty fire - ship, and to her I did steer, I
G E7 Am
hoist - ed up my sig - a - nal which she did quick - ly view, And
D7 G C A7 D C♯dim D7 Chorus
rit.
3
when I had my bunt - ing up She im - med - iate - ly hove to. She had a
G A7 D7
dark and a rov - ing eye, and her hair hung down in ring - e - lets, A
G D7 G E7 Am D7 G
nice girl, a de - cent girl, but one of the rak - ish kind.

G D7
"Excuse me, sir," she said to me, "for being out so late.
G D7
For if my parents knew of this, then sad would be my fate.
G E7 Am
My father is a minister – a good and virtuous man,
D7 G C A7 D C♯dim D7
My mother is a Methodist – I do the best I can." *Chorus*

G D7
I eyed that girl both up and down for I'd heard such talk before,
G D7
And when she moored herself to me, I knew she was a whore.
G E7 Am
But still she was a pretty girl; she shyly hung her head.
D7 G C A7 D C♯dim D7
"I'll go along with you, my lad," this to me she said. *Chorus*

G D7
I took her to a tav-er-in and treated her with wine.
G D7
Oh, little did I ever think that she was of the rakish kind.
G E7 Am
I handled her, I dandled her – but much to my surprise
D7 G C A7 D C♯dim D7
She was only an old pirate ship rigged up in a disguise. *Chorus*

G D7
So up the stairs and into bed I took that maiden fair.
G D7
I fired off my cannon into her thatch of hair.
G E7 Am
I fired off a broadside until my shot was spent,
D7 G C A7 D C♯dim D7
Then rammed that fire ship's waterline until my ram was bent. *Chorus*

G D7
Then in the morning she was gone; my money was gone too.
G D7
My clothes she'd hocked; my watch she stole; my sea bag bid adieu.
G E7 Am
But she'd left behind a souvenir, I'd have you all to know;
D7 G C A7 D C♯dim D7
And in nine days, to my suprise, there was fire down below. *Chorus*

G D7
So listen all you sailor men who sail upon the sea,
G D7
Beware of them there fireships – one was the ruin of me.
G E7 Am
Beware of them, stay clear of them – they'll be the death of you.
D7 G C A7 D C♯dim D7
'Twas there I had my mizzen sprung and my strong-box broken through. *Chorus*

THE FOGGY DEW

G C D7
Well, I am a bach - elor, I live by my - self, I work at the weav - er's
G C
trade.___ And the on - ly thing I ev - er did that was wrong, Was to
D7 G D7 G
woo a fair young maid. I wooed her in the sum - mer - time, And
D7 G
in the win - ter too. But the on - ly thing I ev - er
C A7 D7 G
did that was wrong was to keep her from the fog - gy, fog - gy dew.

G C
One night this maid came to my bed
D7 G
Where I lay fast asleep.
C
She laid her head upon my chest
D7 G
And then began to weep.
D7 G
She sighed, she cried, she damn near died.
D7 G
She said, "What shall I do?"
C A7
So I took her into bed and I covered up her head
D7 G
Just to keep her from the foggy, foggy dew.

G C
All through the first part of the night,
D7 G
We did laugh and play.
C
And through the latter part of the night,
D7 G
She slept in my arms 'til day.
D7 G
Then when the sun shone on our bed,
D7 G
She cried, "I am undone."
C A7
"Hold your tongue, you silly girl.
D7 G
The foggy, foggy dew is gone."

G C
Now I am a bachelor; I live with my son.
D7 G
We work at the weaver's trade,
C
And every time I look into his face
D7 G
He reminds me of the fair young maid.
D7 G
He reminds me of the summer time
D7 G
And of the winter too,
C A7
And the many, many times I took her in my arms
D7 G
Just to keep her from the foggy, foggy dew.

FRANKIE AND JOHNNY

C
Frank - ie and John - ny were lov - ers,
Oh, Lord - y how they could love.
F
Swore to be true to each
oth - er,
Cdim
True as the stars a -
C
bove.
Chorus:
He was her
G7
man,
But he done her
C
wrong.

C
Frankie she was a good girl,

Most everybody knows.
F
She gave a hundred dollars
Cdim C
To Johnny for a suit of clothes. *Chorus*

C
Frankie she worked in a crib-joint

Behind a grocery store.
F
She gave all her money to Johnny;
Cdim C
He spent it on high-tone whores. *Chorus*

C
Frankie was a fucky hussy,

That's what all the pimps said,
F
And they kept her so damn busy.
Cdim C
She never got out of bed. *Chorus*

C
Frankie she sure knew her business,

She hung out a sign on the door:
F
"Fresh fish cost you a dollar here,
Cdim C
Fancy fucking cost ten cents more." *Chorus*

C
Frankie went looking for Johnny.

She hung out a sign on the door:
F
"No more fish for sale now,
Cdim C
Go find you another whore." *Chorus*

C
Frankie went down to Fourth Street.

She ordered a glass of beer,
F
Said to the big bartender man,
Cdim C
"Has my ever-lovin' man been here?" *Chorus*

(continued)

C
"I couldn't tell you no story.

I couldn't tell you no lie.
F
I saw your Johnny an hour ago
Cdim C
With a whore called Alice Bly." *Chorus*

C
Frankie ran back to her crib-joint,

Fixin' to do him some harm.
F
She took out a bindle of horse
Cdim C
And shot it right up her arm. *Chorus*

C
Frankie put on her kimono;

This time it wasn't for fun
F
'Cause right underneath it
Cdim C
Was great big forty-four gun. *Chorus*

C
She ran along Fish Alley,

Looked in a window so high,
F
Saw her lovin' Johnny
Cdim C
Finger-fucking Alice Bly. *Chorus*

C
Frankie went to the front door.

She rang the whorehouse bell.
F
"Stand back you pimps and whores,
Cdim C
Or I'll blow you straight to hell." *Chorus*

C
Frankie drew back her kimono,

Pulled out her big forty-four.
F
Rooty-toot-toot, three times she shoot,
Cdim C
Left him lyin' on that whorehouse floor. *Chorus*

C
"Roll me over, Frankie,

Roll me over slow.
F
A bullet got me in my right side,
Cdim C
Oh God, it hurts me so." *Chorus*

C
Frankie ran back to her crib-joint.

She fell across the bed,
F
Saying, "Lord, oh Lord, I've shot my man.
Cdim C
I've shot my Johnny dead." *Chorus*

C
Three little pieces of crêpe

Hanging on the crib-joint door
F
Signifies that Johnny
Cdim C
Will never be a pimp no more. *Chorus*

C
"Bring out your rubber-tired buggy.

Bring out your rubber-tired hack.
F
I'm taking my man to the graveyard;
Cdim C
I ain't gonna bring him back." *Chorus*

C
They brought out a rubber-tired buggy,

They brought out a rubber-tired hack.
F
Thirteen pimps went to the cemetery,
Cdim C
But only twelve of them came back. *Chorus*

C
Frankie went out to the graveyard,

Sorry as she could be,
F
Ridin' behind a whorehouse band
Cdim C
Playin' "Nearer, My God, to Thee." *Chorus*

```
     C
Frankie stood up in the courtroom.

"I'm not tellin' no sass.
     F
I didn't shoot Johnny in the first degree.
                    Cdim  C
I shot him in his big fat ass."          Chorus


    C
The judge said, "Stand up, Frankie.

Stand up and dry your tears.
   F
You know that murder's a hangin' crime,
                    Cdim          C
But I'll give you ninety-nine years."  Chorus


     C
The last time I seen Frankie

She was ridin' on that train,
   F
Takin' her to the jail house,
                Cdim    C
Never bring her back again.        Chorus
```

THE FRIAR

E
There was a friar of great re - nown, There was a friar
B7 E A
of great re - nown, There was a friar of great re - nown,
tacet chords
3
B7 E
He (spoken) bug - gered a girl in Lon - don town.

E
He took her to the friar's hall,
B7
He took her to the friar's hall,
E A
He took her to the friar's hall,
B7 E
And *buggered her up* against the wall.

E
He laid her down upon his bed,
B7
He laid her down upon his bed,
E A
He laid her down upon his bed,
B7 E
And *buggered her there* till she was dead.

E
He carried her to the burial ground,
B7
He carried her to the burial ground,
E A
He carried her to the burial ground,
B7 E
He *buggered that girl* another round.

E
And when the bells tolled out "Amen,"
B7
And when the bells tolled out "Amen,"
E A
And when the bells tolled out "Amen,"
B7 E
He *buggered her back* to life again.

FUCK 'EM ALL (I)

U.S. Marine Version - Pacific Area, World War II

Verse:
C
They sent for the ar - my to come to Tu -
la - gi, But Gen - er - al Mac - Ar - thur said, "no."
F
And this is the rea - son it is - n't the
G7
sea - son, be - sides, there is no U. S. O.
C
Chorus:
C
Fuck 'em all, fuck 'em all, The long and the
short and the tall.
F
G
Fuck all the ad - mirals who give us the
flak; They don't give a shit if we ev - er come back. So we're
D7
G7

C
say - ing good - bye to them all, As o - ver the
F
G7
gang - plank we crawl. There'll be no pro - mo - tion this
C
side of the o - cean, So cheer up, my lads, fuck 'em all.

C
Oh, they sent for the Navy to come to Tulagi,
F
The gallant Navy agreed.
G7
With one thousand sections in different directions,
C
My God, what a fucked-up stampede. *Chorus*

C
They sent for the nurses to come overseas,
F
The reason was perfectly clear.
G7
To make a good marriage and push a good carriage
C
While fucking all hands, my dear. *Chrous*

FUCK 'EM ALL (II)

U.S. Merchant Marine Version by way of the Royal Air Force in Port Said, Egypt (1942)

Verse:
C
They say there's a con - voy that's leav - ing New York,
G7
Bound for those Bligh - ty* shores; Heav - i - ly la - den with
C
tanks and with planes, Shit for old A - dolf, of course.
So, we're say - ing good - bye to you all, As from
F G7
bar - room to bar - room we crawl. We'll start a com - mo - tion that
C
side of the o - cean, So cheer up, my lads, fuck em' all.

To Chorus (same melody as version I)

Chorus:

C
Fuck 'em all, fuck 'em all,
F
The long and the short and the tall.
G
Fuck all the captains and all the mates too,
D7 G7
Fuck the engineers and the whole God-damn' crew.
C
So, we're saying so long to you all,
F
As off to our rust pots we crawl.
G7
We'll start a commotion that side of the ocean,
C
So, cheer up, my lads, fuck 'em all.

British version, World War II

C
There's many a troop ship just leaving Bombay,
G7
Bound for Old Blighty's shore,
Heavily laden with time-expired men,
C
Bound for the land they adore.

There's many a soldier just finished his time,
F
And many a twerp signing on;
G7
They'll get no promotion this side of the ocean,
C
So cheer up, my lads, fuck 'em all.

*England

```
                    C
Chorus:   Fuck 'em all, fuck 'em all,
                                                   F
          The long and the short and the tall.
           G
          Fuck all the sergeants and W.O. ones*,
           D7                          G7
          Fuck all the corporals and their blinking sons.
                  C
          For we say goodbye to them all,
                                                   F
          As back to the barracks they crawl.
               G7
          You get no promotion this side of the ocean,
                                                      C
          So cheer up, my lads, fuck 'em all.

        C
They say if you work hard you'll get better pay,
                          G7
We've heard it all before.

Clean up your buttons and polish your boots,
                                         C
Scrub out the barrack-room floor.

      There's many a swaddie has taken it in,
                                         F
      Hook, line and sinker and all;
         G7
      You get no promotion this side of the ocean,
                                                 C
      So cheer up, my lads, fuck 'em all.              Chorus

         C
They say that the sergeant's a very nice bloke,
                          G7
Oh, what a tale to tell.

Ask him for leave on a Saturday night –
                                         C
He'll pay your fare home, as well.

      There's many a swaddie has blighted his life
                                                 F
      Through writing rude words on the wall;
         G7
      You get no promotion this side of the ocean,
                                                 G
      So cheer up, my lads, fuck 'em all.              Chorus
```

*"Warrant Officer First Class"

```
C
Officers don't worry me worth a damn.
                    G7
I look the other way.

Bell-bottom trousers with stripes down the side,
                            C
Loafing on combat pay.

      So, we're saying goodbye to them all,
                                              F
      As back to their billets they crawl;
         G7
      You get no promotion this side of the ocean,
                                              C
      So cheer up, my lads, fuck 'em all.              Chorus
```

Here are two good all-purpose choruses which may be affixed to any of the preceeding versions.

```
            C
Fuck 'em all, fuck 'em all,
                                             F
The long and the short and the tall.
 G
Fuck all the blonde cunts and all the brunettes.
 D7                                 G7
Don't be too choosey, just fuck all you gets.
                    C
'Cause we're saying goodbye to them all,
                                  F
As back to barracks we crawl.
       G7
You'll get no erection at short-arm inspection,
                                             C
So prick up, you men, fuck 'em all.

            C
Fuck 'em all, fuck 'em all,
                                             F
The long and the short and the tall.
 G
Fuck all the cunts till you break it in two,
 D7                                 G7
You'll get no loving where you're going to.

And we're saying goodbye to them all,
                                        F
As back to the barracks we crawl.
   G7
So get your big prick up and give it a stick up
                                           C
The cunt or ass hole–fuck 'em all.
```

THE FUCKING MACHINE

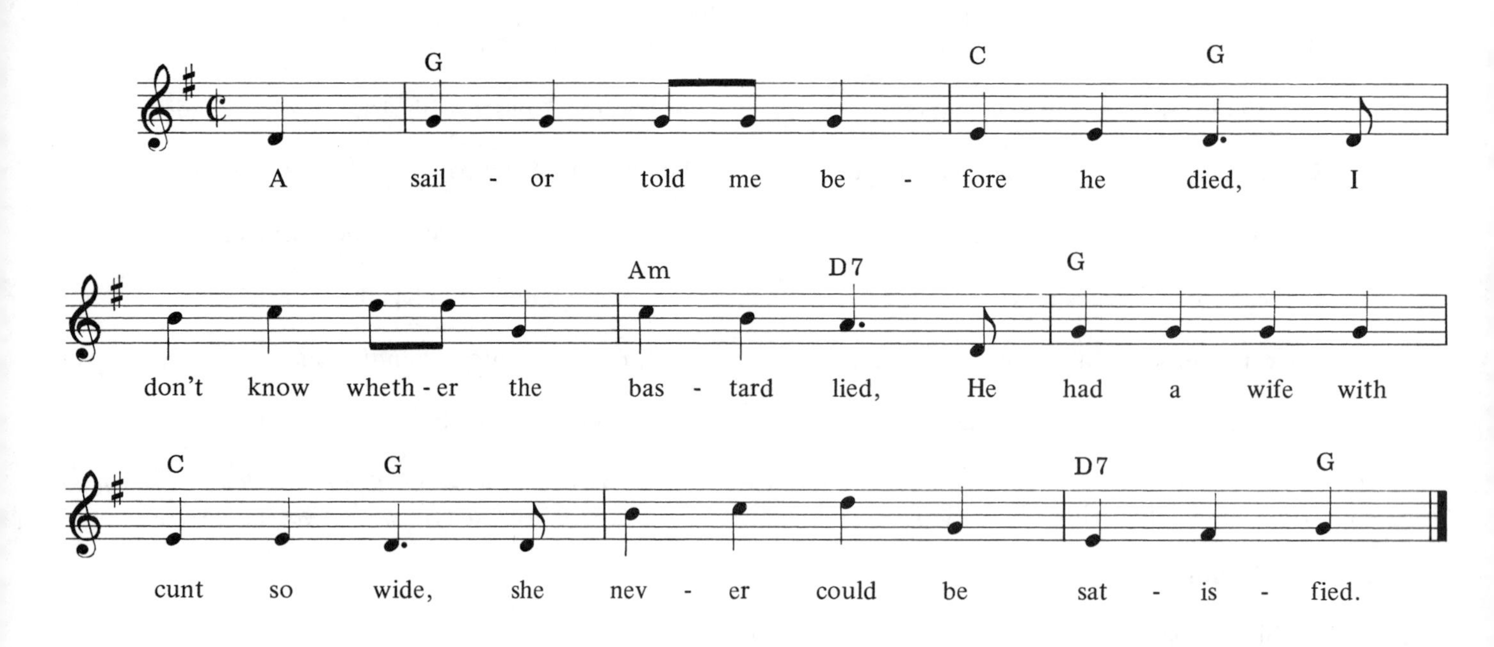
G C G
A sail - or told me be - fore he died, I
Am D7 G
don't know wheth - er the bas - tard lied, He had a wife with
C G D7 G
cunt so wide, she nev - er could be sat - is - fied.

G C G
So he invented a big fucking wheel,
Am D7
Attached to it a big prick of steel.
G C G
Two balls of brass were filled with cream,
D7 G
And the whole fucking thing was run by steam.

G C G
'Round and 'round went the big fucking wheel,
Am D7
In and out went the prick of steel.
G C G
Until at last his wife she cried,
D7 G
"Enough, enough, I'm satisfied."

G C G
But now we come to the bitter bit:
Am D7
There was no way of stopping it.
G C G
The poor girl was ripped from twat to tit,
D7 G
And the whole fucking issue went up in shit.

FUK FAROUK

Sung by members of the British 8th Army stationed in Egypt during World War II.

G
C
Oh, the wogs fuk the dogs and the dogs fuk the wogs, Fuk Fa-
D7
G
rouk, fuk Fa - rouk, Hang his bal - locks on a hook.
E7
Am
Oh, Fa - ree - da, Fuk - ing great lumps of duff.
D7
G
Oh, Fa - ree - da, Fuk - ing great lumps of duff. Oh, Fa -
C
ree - da, oh, Fa - ry - da, How the boys would love to ride 'er, Ma -
D7
G
C
G
leesh, quoi - ski teer, bar - din,* Fuk Fa - rouk!

*"the hell, very good, tomorrow"

Apropos politics, the following was seen on a wall above a public urinal: "You are now holding Nixon by the neck."

GO BRING ME A LASS

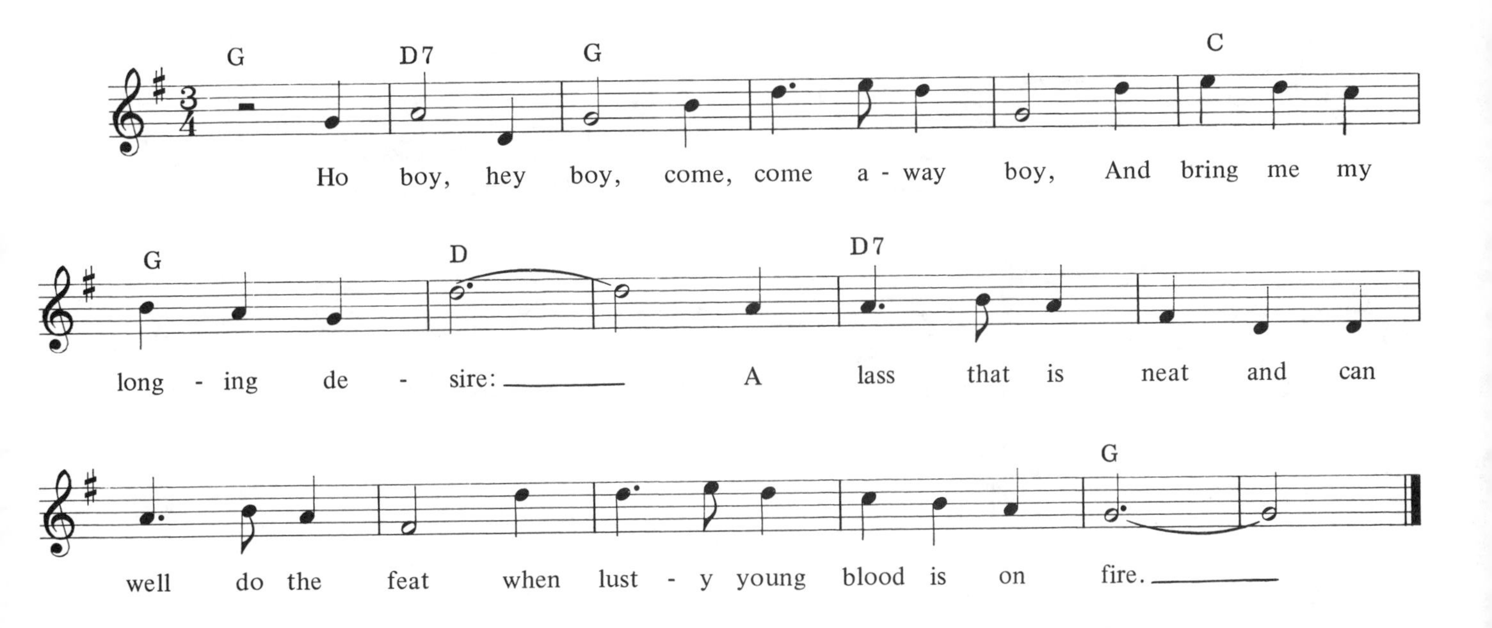

G
D7
G
C
Ho boy, hey boy, come, come a - way boy, And bring me my
G
D
D7
long - ing de - sire: A lass that is neat and can
G
well do the feat when lust - y young blood is on fire.

D7 G
Let her body be tall, let her waist be small,
C G D
And her age not above eighteen;
D7
Let her care for no bed but here let her spread
G
Her mantle upon the green.

D7 G
Let her have cherry lips, where I nectar may sip,
C G D
Let her eyes be as black as a sloe —
D7
Dangling locks I do love, so that those hang above
G
Are the same with what grows below.

D7 G
Let her face be fair, her breasts be bare,
C G D
And a voice let her have that can warble;
D7
Let her belly be soft, but to mount me aloft,
G
Let her bounding buttocks be marble.

THE GOOD SHIP VENUS

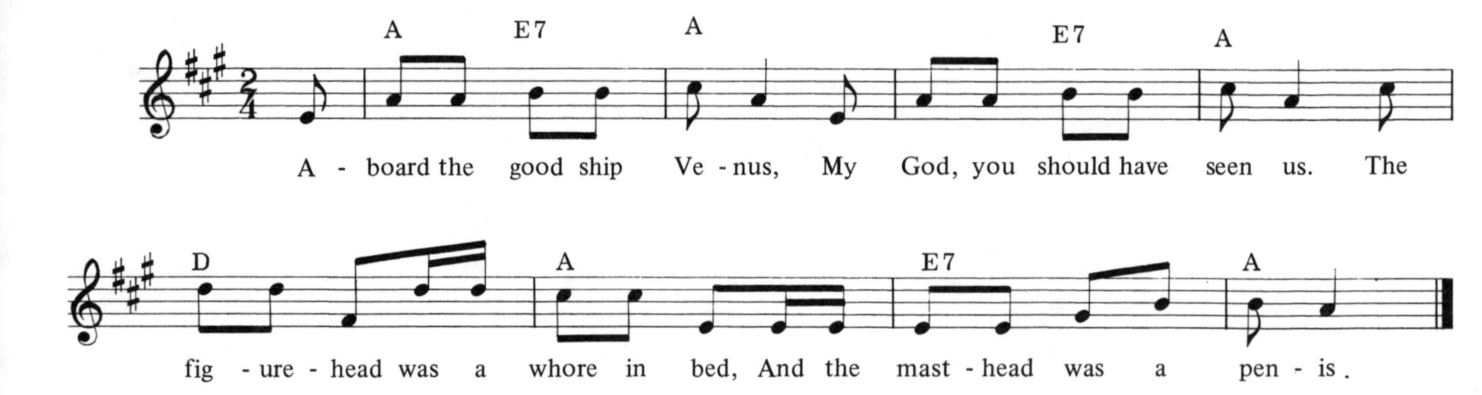
A E7 A E7 A
A - board the good ship Ve - nus, My God, you should have seen us. The
D A E7 A
fig - ure - head was a whore in bed, And the mast - head was a pen - is.

A E7 A
The captain was Carrother,
E7 A
He wept to leave his mother.
D A
He wasn't fit to shovel shit
E7 A
From one place to another.

A E7 A
The first mate's name was Morgan,
E7 A
By God, he was a gorgon.
D A
Ten times a day he'd stop to play
E7 A
With his reproductive organ.

A E7 A
The second mate was Hooper.
E7 A
By God, he was a trooper.
D A
He jerked and jerked until he worked
E7 A
Himself into a stupor.

A E7 A
The bosun's name was Andy.
E7 A
By God, he had a dandy.
D A
They crushed his cock upon a rock
E7 A
For coming in the brandy.

A E7 A
The trip it was exciting,
E7 A
Our pleasures were inviting.
D A
All day we blew – all night we'd screw
E7 A
By artificial lighting.

GREEN GROW THE RASHES

Ascribed to ROBERT BURNS

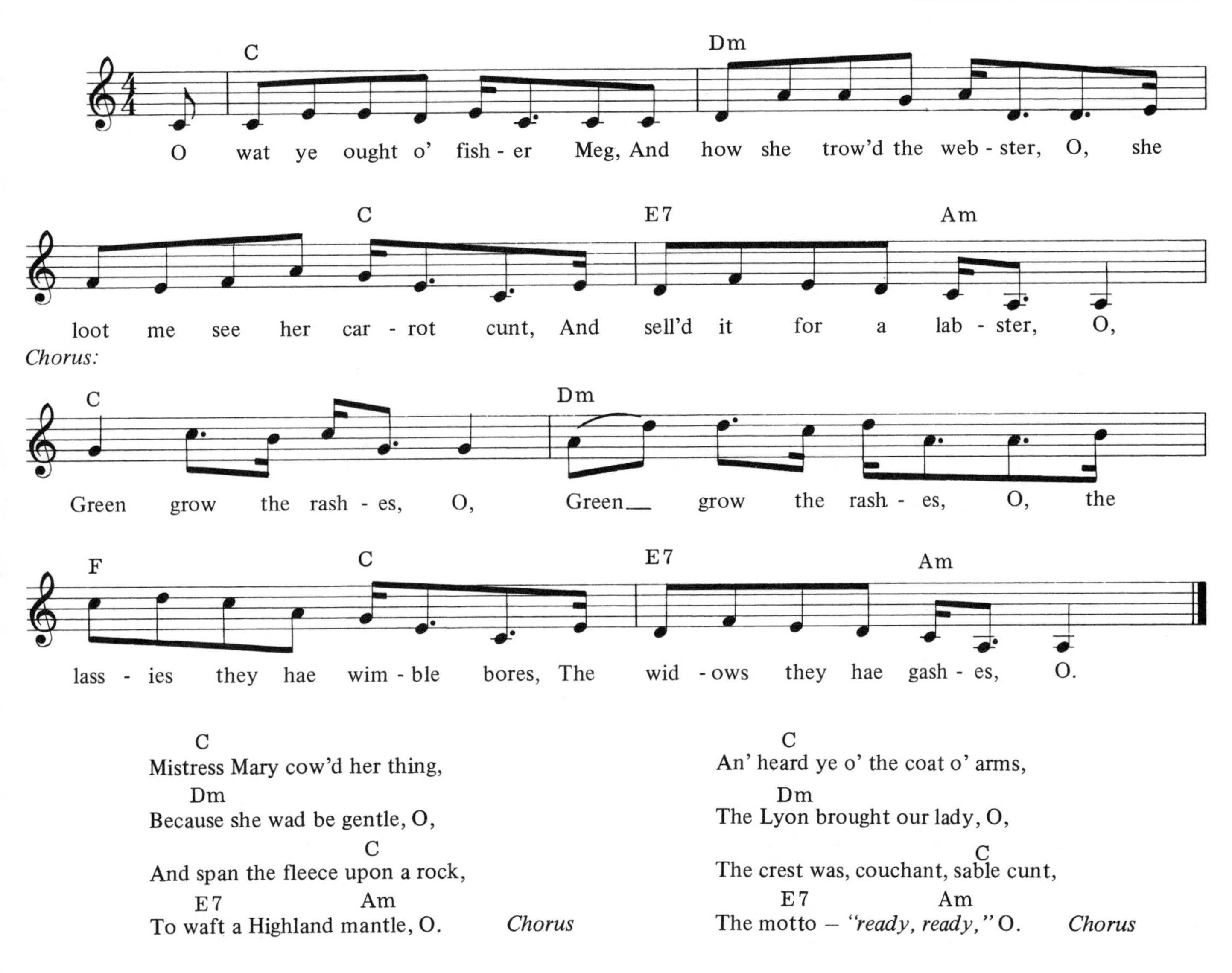

C
Dm
O wat ye ought o' fish - er Meg, And how she trow'd the web - ster, O, she
C
E7
Am
loot me see her car - rot cunt, And sell'd it for a lab - ster, O,
Chorus:
C
Dm
Green grow the rash - es, O, Green__ grow the rash - es, O, the
F
C
E7
Am
lass - ies they hae wim - ble bores, The wid - ows they hae gash - es, O.

C
Mistress Mary cow'd her thing,
Dm
Because she wad be gentle, O,
C
And span the fleece upon a rock,
E7 Am
To waft a Highland mantle, O. *Chorus*

C
An' heard ye o' the coat o' arms,
Dm
The Lyon brought our lady, O,
C
The crest was, couchant, sable cunt,
E7 Am
The motto – *"ready, ready,"* O. *Chorus*

C
An' ken ye Leezie Lundie, O.
Dm
The godly Leezie Lundie, O,
C
She mowes like reek thro' a' the week,
E7 Am
But finger fucks on Sunday, O. *Chorus*

Glossary

wat ye ought	do you know about
trow'd	cursed
webster	weaver
labster	lobster
wimble bores	small holes
cow'd	covered
mowes	fucks
reek	smoke

THE GAY CABALLERO

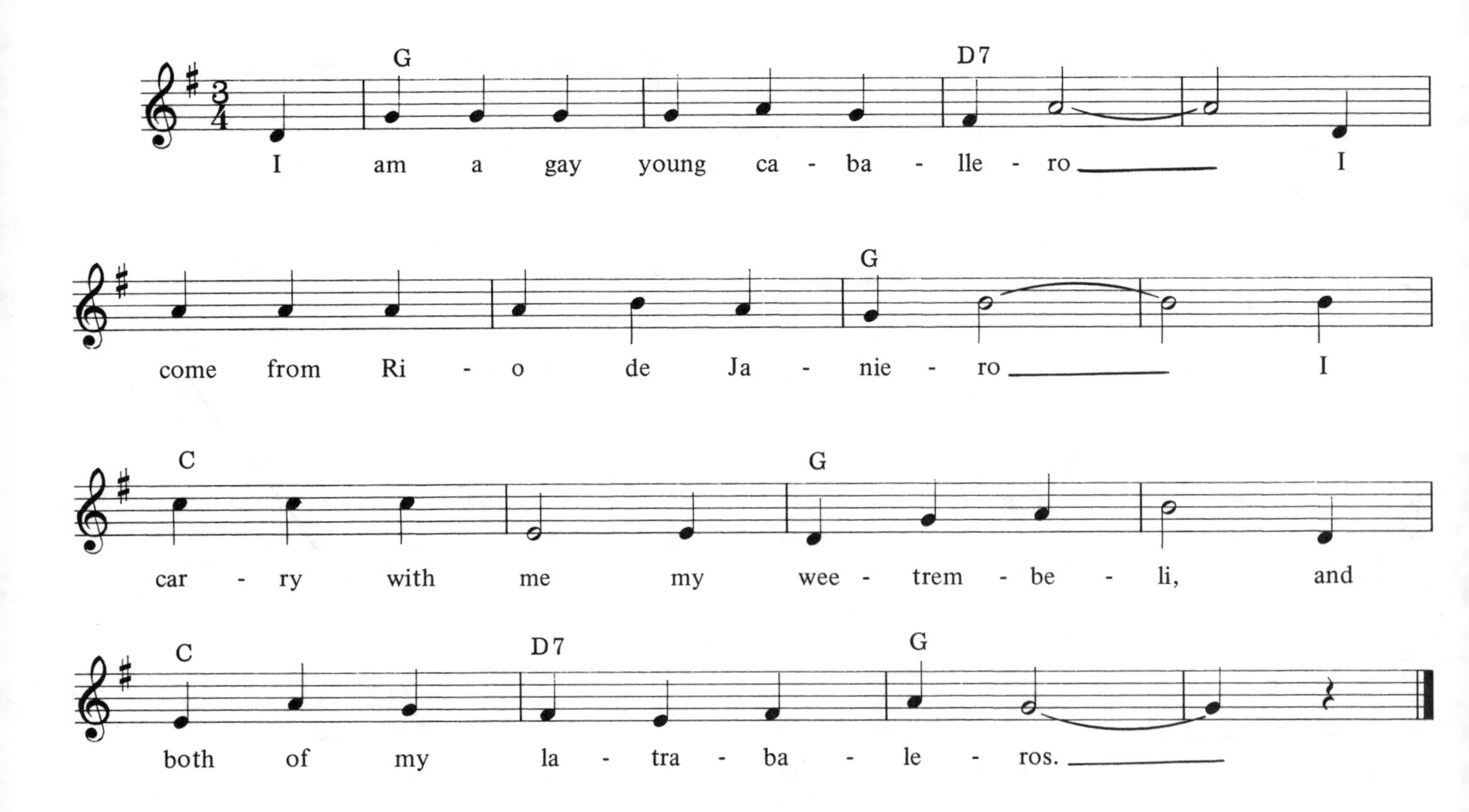
G D7
I am a gay young ca - ba - lle - ro I
G
come from Ri - o de Ja - nie - ro I
C G
car - ry with me my wee - trem - be - li, and
C D7 G
both of my la - tra - ba - le - ros.

G D7
I met a gay young señorita,
G
Who gave me a dose of clapita;
C G
Right on the end of my weetrembeli,
C D7 G
And both of my latrabaleros.

G D7
I went to a wise surgeano,
G
He said, "I prescribe purgeano."
C G
He cut off the end of my weetrembeli,
C D7 G
And both of my latrabaleros.

G D7
And now I'm a sad caballero,
G
Returning to Rio de Janiero.
C G
But not, as you see, with my weetrembeli,
C D7 G
And both of my latrabaleros.

G D7
At night as I lie on my pillow,
G
Seeking to finger my willow.
C G
All I find there is a handful of hair
C D7 G
And one dried up latrabalero.

HAVE YOU GOT A HARD-ON?

This delightful little refrain may be used as a coda for any number of songs in this collection. Just tag it on and milk the applause.

Fast
G
D7
G
D7
Have you got a hard - on? Not yet. Are you gon - na get one? You
G
D7
G
G7
bet. Lis - ten to the whore-house quar - tet: Our balls hang low.

HERE'S TO PAMPA, TEXAS

With a swing
G
D7
Oh, here's to Pam - pa, Tex - as, where the wild wind blows,— Got the
G
fuck - ing - est wo - men that— ev - er wore clothes. Oh, the
D
well's gone dry— and the wheat's give out,— And the
A7
D
Chorus
cock - mind - ed peo - ple go a walk - ing a - bout.— Yo - del -
C
G
D7
G
ay - ee - oh,— Yo - del - ay - ee - oh,— Yo - del - ay ee - oh,— Yo - del - ay - ee.—

```
    G                                  D7
I arrived in Pampa, Texas 'bout the twelfth of June,
                              G
And I said to myself, "This is none too soon."
                                        D
For the likker was a-plenty and the fucking was free;
        A7                              D
And I knew Pampa, Texas was the place for me.            Chorus

       G                       D7
Well, I had soon selected me a pretty little maid,
                                            G
But the temperature it was a hundred-four in the shade.
                                        D
I thought that I would give her everything that I got,
         A7                             D
But the God-damned weather was just too fucking hot.     Chorus

       G                           D7
She looked me in the eye, and she said to me, "Stranger,
                           G
You sure ain't no damn' Texas Ranger.
                          D
If you can't make it, better hit the road."
        A7                        D
I was feelin' mighty foolish as I shot my load.          Chorus

        G                                   D7
So, farewell to Pampa, Texas, where the wild wind blows.
                                            G
Why anyone would live there, goodness only knows.
                                            D
Though the likker was a-plenty and the fucking was free,
          A7                                D
There's better days a-comin', boys, but not for you and me.   Chorus
```

HINKY-DINKY PARLEZ-VOUS?

World War I Army Song

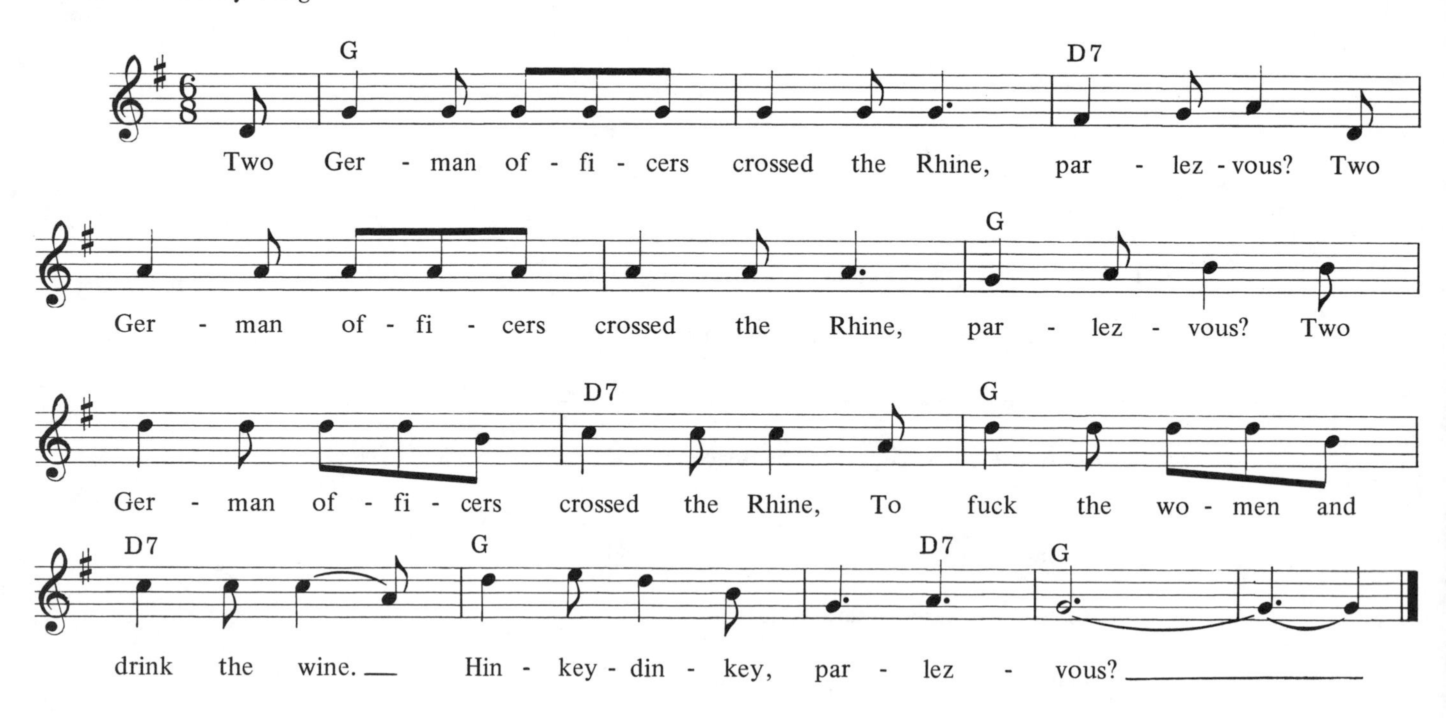
G D7
Two Ger - man of - fi - cers crossed the Rhine, par - lez - vous? Two
G
Ger - man of - fi - cers crossed the Rhine, par - lez - vous? Two
D7 G
Ger - man of - fi - cers crossed the Rhine, To fuck the wo - men and
D7 G D7 G
drink the wine. Hin - key - din - key, par - lez - vous?

```
G                              D7
They came upon a wayside inn, parlez-vous?
                               G
They came upon a wayside inn, parlez-vous?
               D7
They came upon a wayside inn,
G                   D7
Opened the door and walked right in,
 G             D7   G
Hinky, dinky, parlez-vous?
```

```
       G                              D7
Oh, landlord, have you a daughter fair, parlez-vous?
                                         G
Oh, landlord, have you a daughter fair, parlez-vous?
                            D7
Oh, landlord, have you a daughter fair,
      G                    D7
With lily-white tits and golden hair,
 G              D7  G
Hinky-dinky, parlez-vous?
```

```
     G                         D7
Oh, yes, I have a daughter fair, parlez-vous?
                                G
Oh, yes, I have a daughter fair, parlez-vous?
                   D7
Oh, yes, I have a daughter fair,
      G                    D7
With lily-white tits and golden hair,
 G              D7  G
Hinky-dinky parlez-vous?
```

```
     G                                     D7
Oh, can we fuck your daughter fair, parlez-vous?
                                          G
Oh, can we fuck your daughter fair, parlez-vous?
                             D7
Oh, can we fuck your daughter fair,
      G                    D7
With lily-white tits and golden hair,
 G              D7  G
Hinky-dinky parlez-vous?
```

G   D7
Oh, yes, you can have my daughter fair, parlez-vous?
                                         G
Oh, yes, you can have my daughter fair, parlez-vous?
                              D7
Oh, yes you can have my daughter fair,
  G   D7
With lily-white tits and golden hair,
  G   D7   G
Hinky-dinky parlez-vous?

     G   D7
They fucked her on the table there, parlez-vous?
                                      G
They fucked her on the table there, parlez-vous?
                          D7
They fucked her on the table there,
  G   D7
There were tits and hair to spare,
  G   D7   G
Hinky-dinky parlez-vous?

  G   D7
Madamoiselle from Armentières parlez-vous?
                                  G
Madamoiselle from Armentières parlez-vous?
                         D7
Madamoiselle from Armentières,
  G   D7
Hasn't been fucked in forty years,
  G   D7   G
Hinky-dinky parlez-vous?

LADY ARRHEE

LADY SENTRIE

HUMORESQUE

Music by **A. DVORAK**
Words—**no one will admit it**

C
F
Pas - sen - gers will please re - frain from us - ing toi - lets while the train is
C
Am
D7 G7
C
in the sta - tion, dar - ling I love you. There - fore we urge con - sti - pa - tion
F
F♯dim
Cm
F♯dim
G7
C
when the train is in the sta - tion if the train can't go then why should you?

C
My favorite pastime after dark
F
Is goosing statues in the park.
C Am
If Sherman's horse can take it,
D7 G7
Why can't you?
C
I'm the guy that did the pushin',
F F♯dim
Put the stains upon the cushion;
Cm F♯dim
Footprints on the dashboard
G7 C
Upside down.

C
When you have a natural urge,
F
Or after you have had a purge,
C Am
The management requests
D7 G7
You learn the art
C
Of using roses or wisteria
F F♯dim
'Tween the parts of your posterior:
Cm F♯dim
Guaranteed to camo -
G7 C
Flage a fart.

C
When you have to pass some water,
F
Do it in the place you oughter.
C Am
Please don't use my hat,
D7 G7
And be a pal.
C
Picture, please, your consternation,
F F♯dim
And your righteous indignation
Cm F♯dim
If you found your hat
G7 C
A urinal.

C
Nothing looks much better
F
Than a girl who wears a sweater,
C Am
Though she may not be as big as
D7 G7
She appears.
C
Remember, boys, before you wed 'er,
F F♯dim
Better look inside the sweater —
Cm F♯dim
Or your wedding night
G7 C
May end in tears.

HITLER HAS ONLY GOT ONE BALL

The Colonel Bogey March

Sung by brave British soldiers everywhere as they marched along, but only whistled in the film, *The Bridge Over The River Kwai.*

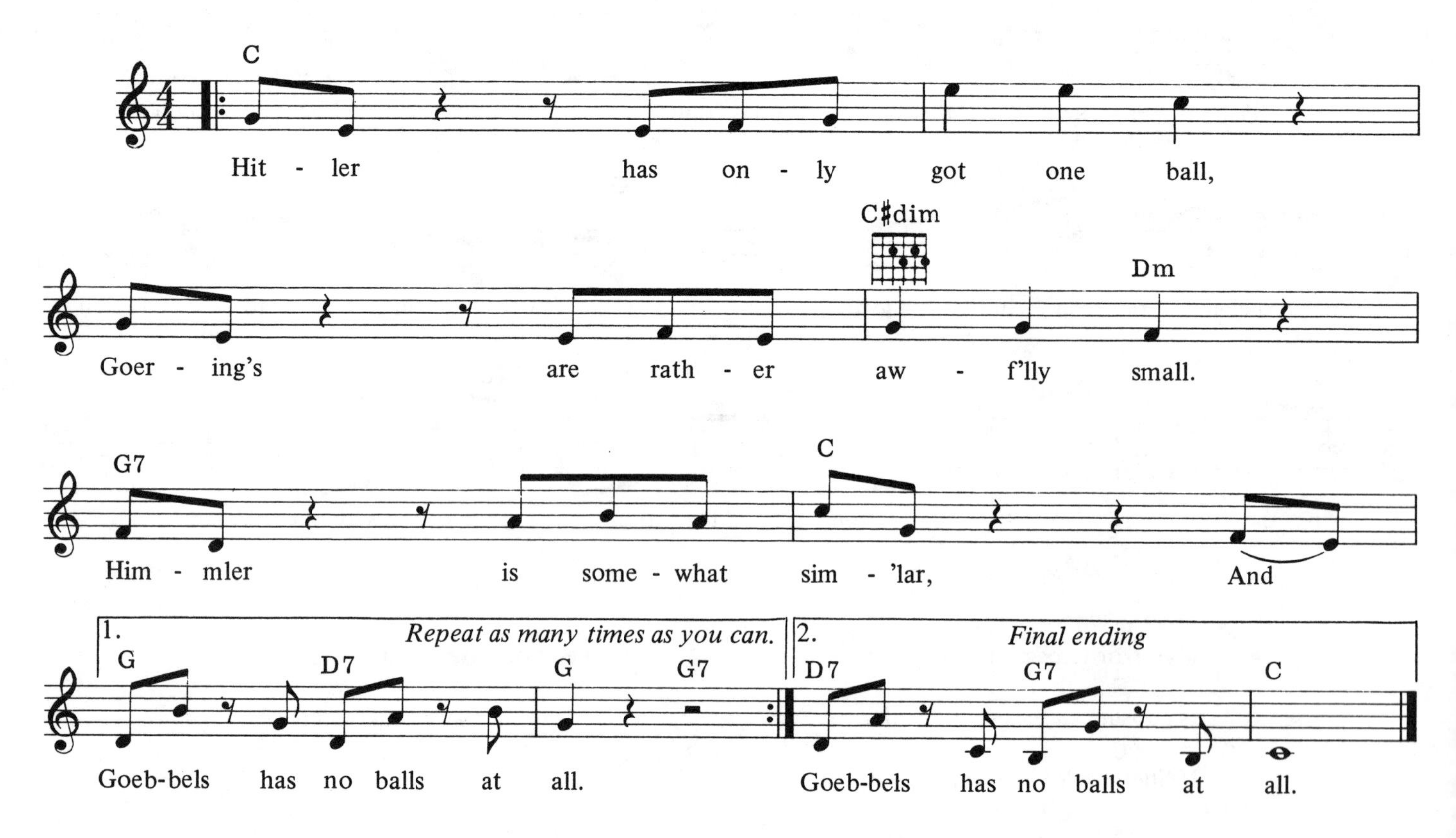

C
Hit - ler has on - ly got one ball,
C♯dim
Dm
Goer - ing's are rath - er aw - f'lly small.
G7
C
Him - mler is some - what sim - 'lar, And
1.
Repeat as many times as you can.
G D7 G G7
Goeb-bels has no balls at all.
2.
Final ending
D7 G7 C
Goeb-bels has no balls at all.

I DON'T WANT TO JOIN THE ARMY

Mon - day, I touched her on the shoul - der, Tues - day, I touched her on the
knees. We'n's-day, with suc - cess, I ___ lift - ed up her dress, Thurs - day, her chem -
ise. (Gor blim - ey!) Fri - day, I put me hand up - on it,
Sat - ur - day, she gave me balls a tweak. And ___ Sun - day af - ter sup - per, I
rammed the damn' thing up her, And now I'm earn - ing ten and six a
To verse 2
week. (Gor blim - ey!) for - ni - cate me fuck - ing life a - way!

I don't want to join the army,
I don't want to go to war.
I'd rather hang around Picadilly Underground,
Living off the earnings of me high-born lady.
I don't want a bullet up me arse hole,
I don't want me ballocks shot away.
I'd rather stay in England –
In ruddy, bloody England,
And fornicate me fucking life away.

IT'S THE SAME THE WHOLE WORLD OVER

Chorus:
E A B7
It's the same the whole world o - ver, It's the poor what gets the
E A B7 E
blame; While the rich has all the plea-sures, Now, ain't that a fuck - ing shame?

```
    E              A
She was poor, but she was honest,
     B7            E
Pure unstained was her fame.
                            A
Till a country squire come courting,
      B7              E
And the poor girl lost her name. Chorus

   E              A
So she went away to London,
     B7             E
Just to hide her guilty shame.
                            A
There she met an Army Chaplain –
   B7                E
Once again she lost her name. Chorus

     E                 A
Hear him as he jaws the Tommies,
     B7            E
Warning of the devil's flame.
                                A
With her whole heart she had trusted,
     B7               E
But again she lost her name. Chorus

     E                A
So she settled down in London,
      B7             E
Sinking deeper in her shame,
                    A
Till she met a labor leader,
      B7               E
And again she lost her name. Chorus

        E                     A
Now he's in the House of Commons,
        B7                    E
Making laws to put down crime;
                             A
While the victim of his pleasure
          B7                         E
Walks the streets each night in shyme. Chorus

        E           A
See him riding in his carriage,
        B7           E
See him going to the hunt;
                           A
Thinking nothing of a marriage,
       B7          E
Only of a piece of cunt. Chorus

          E            A
See him passing in his carriage
          B7                       E
With his face all wreathed in smiles.
                            A
See her sitting on the pavement,
             B7          E
Which is bloody bad for piles. Chorus

            E           A
You'll find her in the theayter,
          B7         E
See her sitting in the stalls.
                            A
And at home an hour later,
           B7                        E
Playing with some stranger's balls. Chorus
```

E A
See her on the bridge at midnight,
B7 E
Gazing sadly at the moon.
A
She said, "Sir, I've never 'ad it."
B7 E
But she spoke too fucking soon. *Chorus*

E A
Standing on the bridge at midnight,
B7 E
Squeezing blackheads from her crotch,
A
She said, "Jack, I've never 'ad it."
B7 E
I said, "No, not fucking much." *Chorus*

E A
Standing on a bridge at midnight,
B7 E
Selling matches from a box.
A
She said, "Sir, I've never 'ad it."
B7 E
I said, "No, you've got the pox." *Chorus*

E A
In a cottage down in Sussex
B7 E
Lives her parents, old and lame.
A
And they drink the wine she sends them,
B7 E
But they never speaks her name. *Chorus*

E A
In their poor and humble dwelling,
B7 E
There her grieving parents live.
A
Sipping champagne as she sends them,
B7 E
But they never can forgive. *Chorus*

I WAS HAVING TROUBLE SEEING MARY

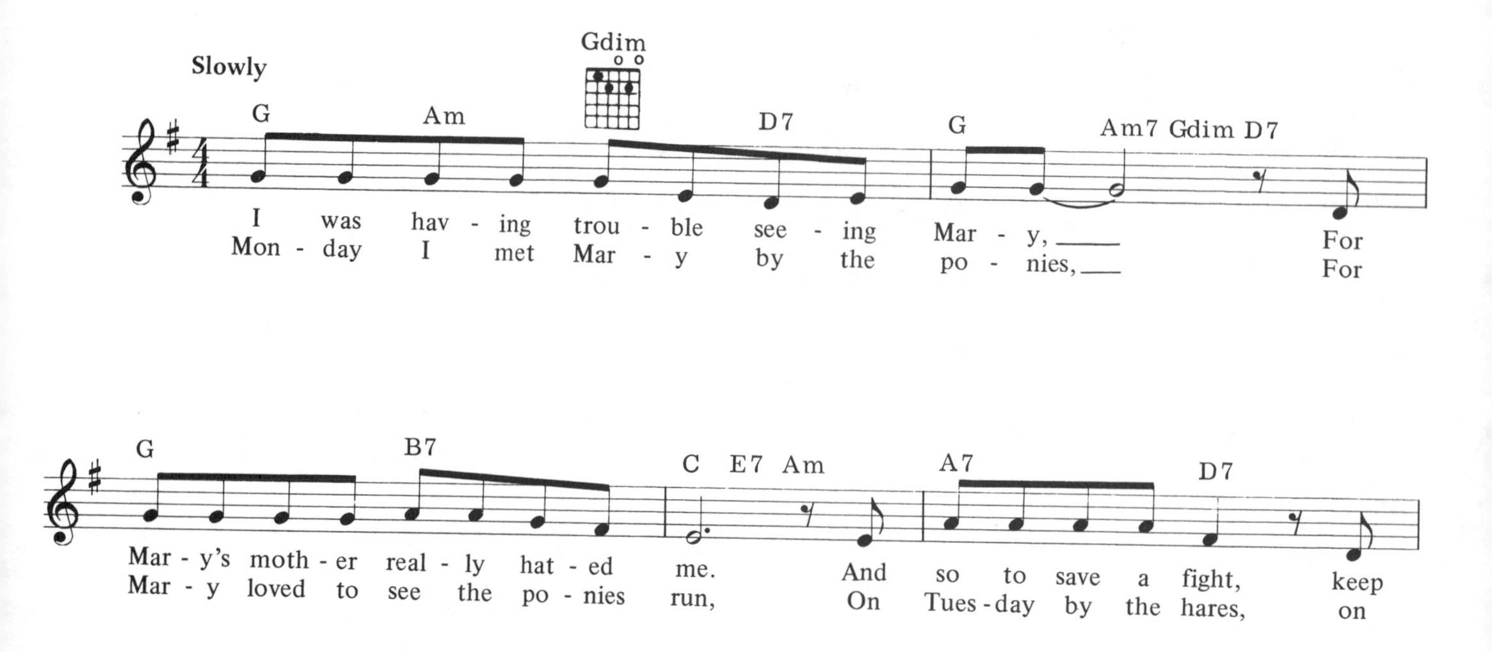
Slowly
Gdim
G Am D7 G Am7 Gdim D7
I was hav - ing trou - ble see - ing Mar - y, For
Mon - day I met Mar - y by the po - nies, For
G B7 C E7 Am A7 D7
Mar - y's moth - er real - ly hat - ed me. And so to save a fight, keep
Mar - y loved to see the po - nies run, On Tues - day by the hares, on

G B7 Em Em7 A7 Adim Em A7
ev - 'ry - thing al - right, I was meet - ing Mar - y by the
We'n's - day by the bears, Thurs - day by the an - te - lopes we
D7 Ddim D7 D. C. Em C9
za - zu, za - zu zoo. Fri - day I met Mar - y by the
had a lot of fun.
G C7 G B7
mon - kies, Swing - ing on their lit - tle rings of
C E7 Am Cm6 C7-5 Daug7 G Gb 3fr F E7
brass. Sat - ur - day, I met her by the don - kies, And
A7 D7 G B7 Dm6 E7 E7-5
that's when I had Mar - y by the As you de - sire it,
A7 D7 ritard G G7 Gdim Cm6 G
That's when I had Mar - y by the za - zu, za - zu, zass.
Guitar

KATHUSALEM

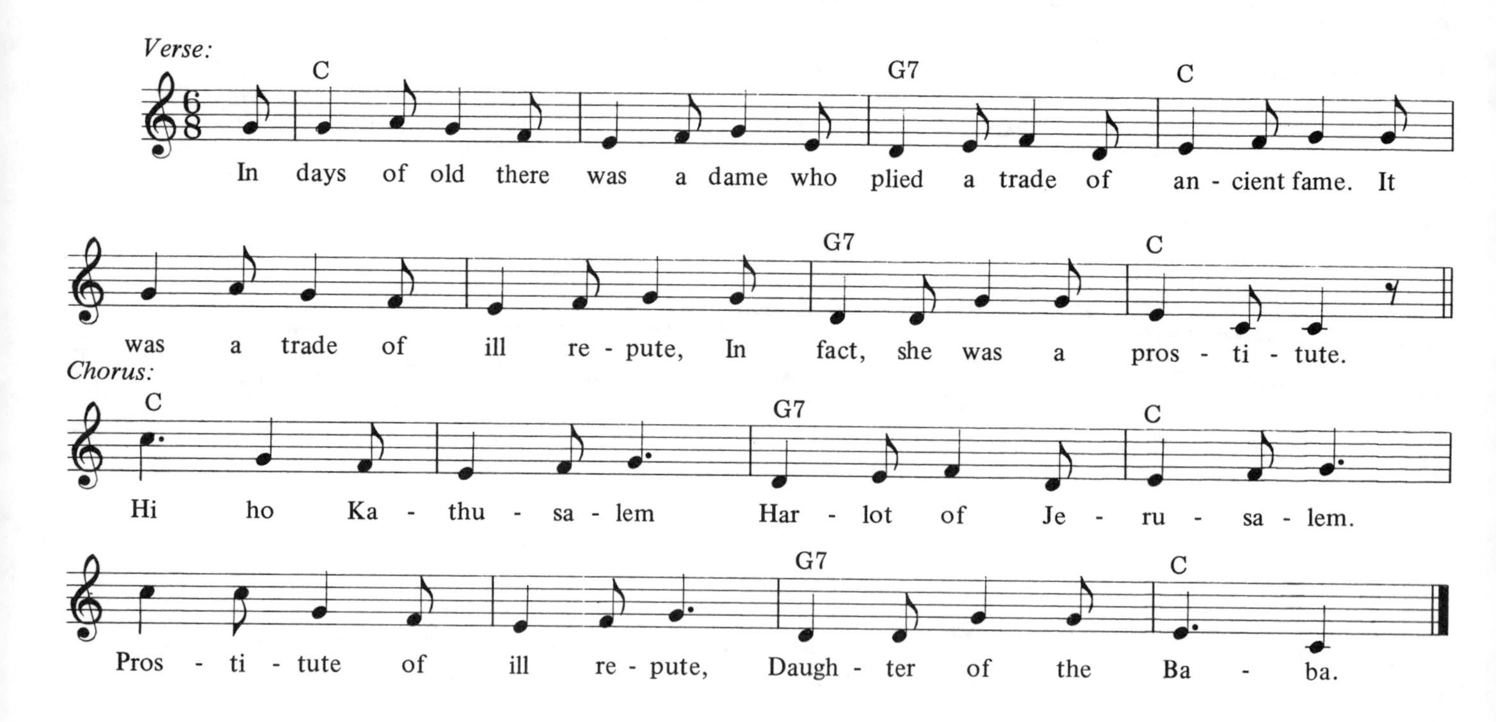
Verse:
C G7 C
In days of old there was a dame who plied a trade of an - cient fame. It
G7 C
was a trade of ill re - pute, In fact, she was a pros - ti - tute.
Chorus:
C G7 C
Hi ho Ka - thu - sa - lem Har - lot of Je - ru - sa - lem.
G7 C
Pros - ti - tute of ill re - pute, Daugh - ter of the Ba - ba.

C
Kathusalem was a wily witch,
G7 C
A fucking whore, a dirty bitch.

She maketh all the pricks to itch –
G7 C
This harlot of Jerusalem. *Chorus*

C
It was a fact, she had a crack
G7 C
With hair of black that could contract

To fit the tool of any fool
G7 C
Who fucked in all Jerusalem. *Chorus*

C
And now within this city's wall
G7 C
There dwelt a priest both lean and tall,

And he had fucked them one and all,
G7 C
The maidens of Jerusalem. *Chorus*

C
One night returning from a spree,
G7 C
His customary hard had he,

Looked down the road and chanced to see
G7 C
The harlot of Jerusalem. *Chorus*

C
She took him to a shady nook,
G7 C
And from its hiding place he took

His pecker – how it throbbed and shook –
G7 C
The pride of all Jerusalem. *Chorus*

C
He laid her down upon the grass,
G7 C
Lifted her dress above her ass,

He grabbed his prick and made a pass
G7 C
Directly at Kathusalem. *Chorus*

C
But she was low and underslung,
G7 C
He missed her twat and hit her bung,

Planting the seeds of many a son
G7 C
In the ass hole of Kathusalem. *Chorus*

C
Kathusalem, she knew her art;
G7 C
She arched her back and blew a fart,

And blew the bastard all apart,
G7 C
All over old Jerusalem. *Chorus*

C
And when the moon is bright and red,
G7 C
A tattered form sails overhead,

And rains down curses on the bed
G7 C
Of the brazen bitch, Kathusalem. *Chorus*

LADY CHATTERLY'S LOVER

D
Oh, I am a game keep - er and I'm
up from Not - ting - ham - shire,
A7
I served my mas - ter
faith - ful - ly, though his wife was rath - er queer,
D
For
one day in the pot - ting shed she asked me for some game,
A7
May - be I mis - took her, but it were fun just the same.
D
Chorus
With my
deer - stalk - er hat and my fol the did - dle - dee,
A7
I was the lov - er of La - dy Chat - ter - ly.
D

D
We had a game of blind-man's bluff,
A7
She landed on the grass.

She looked so pretty lying there,
D
And so I made a pass.

She didn't seem to mind it –
A7
In fact it went to her head.

She pulled me into me cottage
D
And she pushed me into bed. *Chorus*

D
After we had finished
A7
What has since been called "a bout,"

This pretty young maid leapt out of bed,
D
And then began to shout,

"There's that dirty D. H. Lawrence,
A7
A-peeping 'round the door."

He was off before I could get me gun,
D
And he wrote down all he saw. *Chorus*

D
She said the aristocracy
A7
Should mingle with the folk.
She mingled alright with me all night,
D
It got beyond a joke.
Her husband couldn't please her,
A7
Said he, it was the war.
Said I to meself, "He's gone on strike,
D
He knows what he's in for." *Chorus*

D
They wouldn't let him publish it
A7
Because it was pornographic,
But travelers brought it from abroad
D
And did a roaring traffic.
Then Penguin took the case to court
A7
And had a stroke of luck:
"Educational," said the jury,
D
Knowing words like "love a duck." *Chorus*

D
I still think of her,
A7
Although her sins are scarlet.
She befriended a working man like I,
D
And now she's called a harlot.
As for Sir Clifford,
A7
He's given me the sack,
Since he read about what happened in bed
D
In a Penguin paperback. *Chorus*

LA PIERREUSE
The Low-Class Prostitute
Refrain (Chorus):
French Medical Student Song
Fous la au lit, fous la par ter - re, Fous la là
Fuck her in bed, or in the gar - den, An - y - thing
où - 'sque tu vou - dras, 'Sque tu vou - dras. Soit par - de - vant, soit par der -
goes, she is no saint, She is no saint. Ei - ther in front, or from the
riè - re, Ja - mais la garc' ne s'en plain - dra. Je
rear end, She'll nev - er make an - y com - plaint. I
Verse
fais le trot - toir rue d'la Lu - ne; Je taille une plume pour
work the side - walks ev - 'ry night and day; I suck all com - ers
un é - cu, Pour un é - cu. Dans c'mé - tier - là pour
as they pass, As they pass. To make this lous - y,
fair - e for - tu - ne, Il faut sa - voir jou - er du cul.
fuck - ing bus - 'ness pay, You've got to make it with your ass.
Avec des marlous d' bas étage
Je fais des noc's à tout casser,
(à tout casser).
Et c' qui m'épat, c'est qu'à mon âge
Je puiss' encor' les fair' bander! Refrain
I spend the most exhausting nights
With all those low-down, no-good guys,
(those no-good guys).
And at my age it's a big surprise,
That I can still make their pricks rise. Chorus
Au coin du Faubourg Poissonnière,
Quand un miche me fait de l'oeil,
(me fait de l'oeil),
Il faut me voir pimpante et fière:
Jamais putain n'eut plus d'orgueil! Refrain
On the corner of the street,
When some big stiff gives me the eye,
(gives me the eye),
I tell you, I am hard to beat;
Never a whore as proud as I. Chorus
102

D
Y m' fout su' l' lit, pan! v'là qu'l m'baise;
E7 A7
Et, pendant qu'il s'esquinte à jouir,
E7 A7
(s'esquinte à jouir),
D
Je fais la chasse à la punaise,
A7 D
Afin d'pouvoir la nuit dormir. *Refrain*

D
J'en suis encor' toute esquintée;
E7 A
L'avait-il gros, ce vieux paillard!
E7 A7
(ce vieux paillard!).
D
J'ai cru que j'allais éclater
A7 D
Pendant qu'il m'enfonçait son dard. *Refrain*

D
S'il me l'avait foutu' dans l'ventre,
E7
J'aurais bien pu ne pas l' sentir,
E7 A7
(ne pas l'sentir);
D
Mais quand c'est dans l' cul qu' ça vous rentre,
A7 D
Bordel de Dieu! qu' ça fait souffrir. *Refrain*

D
Je vous le dis en confidence:
E7 A
Les hommes, ça n'est pas c' qui nous faut,
E7 A7
(pas c' qui nous faut),
D
Ça vous procure trop peu d' jouissance
A7 D
Pour tout le mal que ça nous vaut. *Refrain*

D
Un frais vagin, c'est autre chose;
E7 A
On l' suce, on lui fait mille horreurs,
E7 A7
(fait mille horreurs),
D
Puis on l'efeuille comme une rose,
A7 D
Comme si c'était un bouquet d' fleurs! *Refrain*

D
Right into bed, pow! he shoves it in,
E7 A
And while he's fucking me – the creep,
E7 A7
(the dirty creep),
D
The hunt for bedbugs does begin,
A7 D
So later I can get some sleep. Chorus

D
This time it really was the worst.
E7 A
He had a big one – long and thick,
E7 A7
(too long and thick).
D
The bastard almost made me burst
A7 D
While he was shoving in his prick. Chorus

D
If he had fucked me from the front,
E7 A
It never would have hurt a bit.
E7 A7
(never a bit).
D
But they prefer the ass hole to the cunt.
A7 D
It hurts like hell – and that's no shit. Chorus

D
I'll tell you confidentially,
E7 A
Those men are not worth all that fuss,
E7 A7
(worth all that fuss).
D
Too little pleasure we receive,
A7 D
For all the pain that they give us. Chorus

D
A fresh vagina always goes –
E7 A
They suck it for what seems like hours,
E7 A7
(it seems like hours).
D
And then they pluck it like a rose –
A7 D
Just like it's a bouquet of flowers. Chorus

Since you are obviously interested in foreign tongues you should find this unusual piece of subway graffito rather stimulating.

Dictionary

ENGLISH	DANSK
prick	pek
cunt	fisse
balls	pongkugeler
shame lips	skamlaeber
ass hole	røvhul
fuck	kut

LIMERICKS

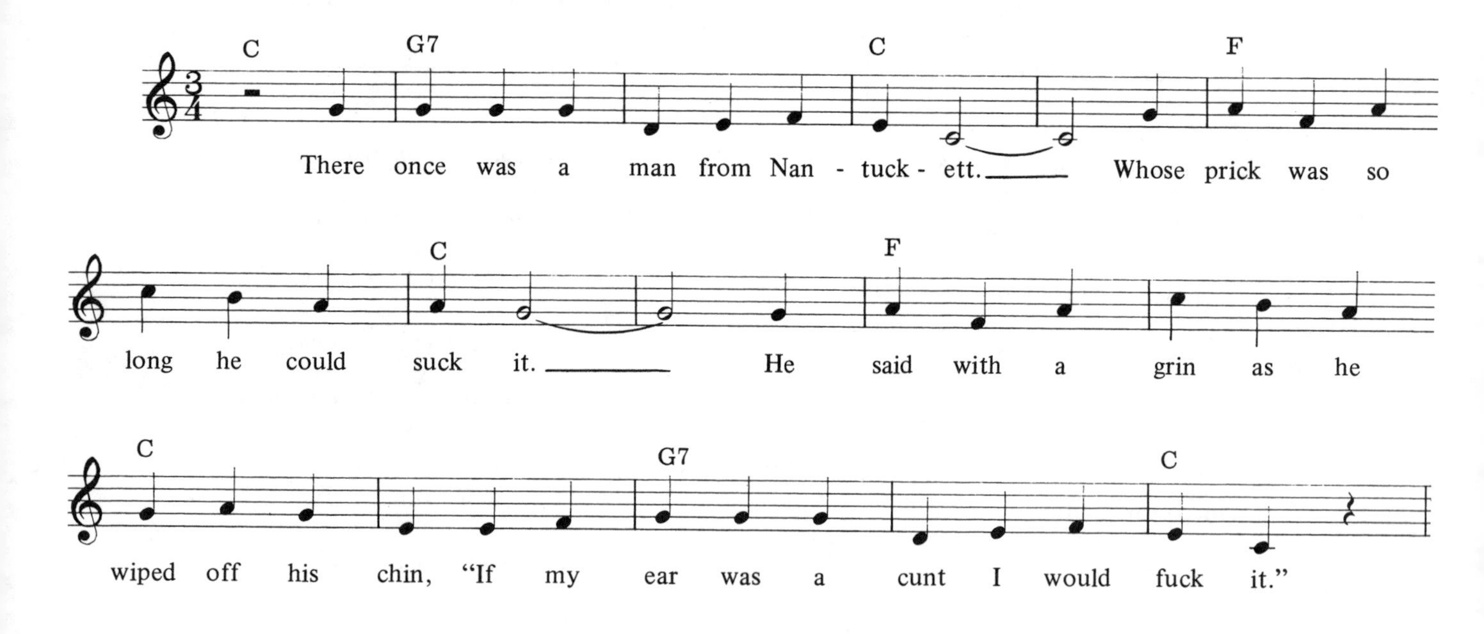
C G7 C F
There once was a man from Nan - tuck - ett. Whose prick was so
C F
long he could suck it. He said with a grin as he
C G7 C
wiped off his chin, "If my ear was a cunt I would fuck it."

G7 C
There once was a monk from Siberia
F C
Whose life it grew drearier and drearier.
F
He did to a nun
C
What he shouldn't have done,
G7 C
And now she's a mother superior.

G7 C
There once was a hermit named Dave
F C
Who kept a dead whore in his cave.
F
He said, "I'll admit
C
I'm a bit of a shit,
G7 C
But look at the money I save."

G7 C
There was a young fellow from Kent
F C
Whose prick was so long that it bent.
F
To save himself trouble
C
He put it in double,
G7 C
And instead of coming – he went.

G7 C
There was a young man from Racine
F C
Who invented a fucking machine.
F
Concave or convex,
C
It would fit either sex,
G7 C
And jerk itself off in between.

G7 C
There was a young man named Carter,
F C
The world's most prodigious farter.
F
He could fart anything,
C
From "God Save The King,"
G7 C
To Beethoven's "Moonlight Sonata."

G7 C
There was a young lady from Dee,
F C
Whose hymen was split into three.
F
And when she was diddled,
C
The middle string fiddled,
G7 C
"Nearer, My God, To Thee."

G7 C
A Scotsman who lived by the Loch,
F C
Had holes down the length of his cock.
F
When he got an erection,
C
He would play a selection
G7 C
From Johann Sebastian Bach.

G7 C
There was a young couple named Kelly,
F C
Who once got stuck belly to belly.
F
Because in their haste,
C
They used library paste
G7 C
Instead of petroleum jelly.

G7 C
An Argentine gaucho named Bruno
F C
Said, "Fucking is one thing I do know.
F
All women are fine,
C
And sheep are divine,
G7 C
But llamas are *numero uno*."

G7 C
There was a young man from Paree,
F C
Who buggered an ape in a tree.
F
The result was quite horrid,
C
All ass and no forehead,
G7 C
Three balls and a purple goatee.

G7 C
There was a young man named Adair
F C
Who was fucking a girl on the stair.
F
The banister broke.
C
But he doubled his stroke,
G7 C
And polished her off in mid-air.

G7 C
The new cinematic emporium
F C
Is not just a super sensorium,
F
But a highly effectual,
C
Heterosexual,
G7 C
Mutual masterbatorium.

G7 C
"For the tenth time, dull Daphne," said Chloë,
F C
"You have told me my bosom is snowy.
F
You have made much fine verse on
C
Each part of my person;
G7 C
Now do something – there's a good boy"

G7 C
There once was a fairy named Bloom,
F C
Who took a queer up to his room.
F
They fought half the night
C
To see who had the right
G7 C
To do what, where and how to whom.

LONG AND THIN

Children's Song

Tune: POP GOES THE WEASEL
C G7 C G7
Long and thin goes too ___ far in, And does - n't please the
C G7 C
la - dies; Short and thick will do ___ the trick, And
F G7 C D7
bring out prop - er ba - bies. O - ur Mar - y
G D7 G F
tried _ it once, Once is once too man - y; Was - n't she a
D7 G7 C
prop - er dunce? Did it for a pen - ny.

THE MAIDEN'S PLAINT

Another aspect of the Battle of Britain

Tune: **CLEMENTINE**

G
In a crowd - ed air - raid shel - ter, In a black - out came a
D7 G D7 G
squeal; 'Twas the plaint of a fair maid - en, 'Cause a strang - er stole a feel.

G
'Twas a new thrill to this lassie,
D7
To be touched in such a way.
G
She but sensed it was immoral,
D7 G
But she liked it – lackaday.

G
Something new was quickly added,
D7
She was held as in a trance.
G
When the all-clear whistle sounded
D7 G
Someone had been in her pants.

G
Why should he with all his money,
D7
Pick on her who was so poor?
G
Bring disgrace upon her family,
D7 G
Making her a goddamned whore!

G
See him in the House of Commons,
D7
Making laws for all mankind,
G
While she walks the streets of Dover,
D7 G
Selling chunks of her behind.

G
But now, friends, my story changes,
D7
Proving justice will prevail;
G
Some years later, while in Dover,
D7 G
This M.P. was after tail.

G
Neither person knew the other,
D7
Here was retribution's trap –
G
When this M.P. for a pound note
D7. G
Got from her a dose of clap.

G
See him suffering as it itches,
D7
See him suffering as it burns.
G
See her with her new-found riches –
D7 G
Thus it is that fortune turns.

MAIDS, WHEN YOU'RE YOUNG NEVER WED AN OLD MAN

G D7
An old man came court - in' me, Hey dum doo - rum down An
G D7
old man came court - in' me, Hey doo - rum down An
G D7 G D7 G
old man came court - in' me, Fain would he mar - ry me, Maids, when you're
C D7 G
Chorus:
young, nev - er wed an old man. For he's got no fa - loo - ral, fa -
D7 G
lid - dle fa - loo - ral, He's got no fa - loo - ral fa - lid - dle all
D7 G D7 G
day, He's got no fa - loo - rum, He's lost his ding -
D7 G C D7 G
doo - rum, So maids, when you're young, nev - er wed an old man.

G
When we went to the church,
D7
Hey dum doorum down.
G
When we went to the church,
D7
Hey doorum down.
G D7
When we went to the church,
G D7
He left me in the lurch,
G C D7 G
Maids, when you're young, never wed an old man. *Chorus*

G
And when we went to bed
D7
Hey dum doorum down.
G
And when we went to bed,
D7
Hey doorum down.
G D7
And when we went to bed,
G D7
He neither done nor said.
G C D7 G
Maids, when you're young never wed an old man. *Chorus*

G
When he went off to sleep
              D7
Hey dum doorum down.
G
When he went off to sleep,
                    D7
Hey doorum down.
G   D7
When he went off to sleep,
G   D7
Out of bed I did creep,
G   C   D7   G
Into the arms of a handsome young man.

Final Chorus:
           G   D7
And I found his falooral falidddle falooral,
   G   D7
I found his falooral faliddle all day.
   G   D7   G   D7
I found his faloorum, he got my dingdoorum.
    G   C   D7   G
So, maids, when you're young, never wed an old man.

THE MAN WHO COMES AROUND

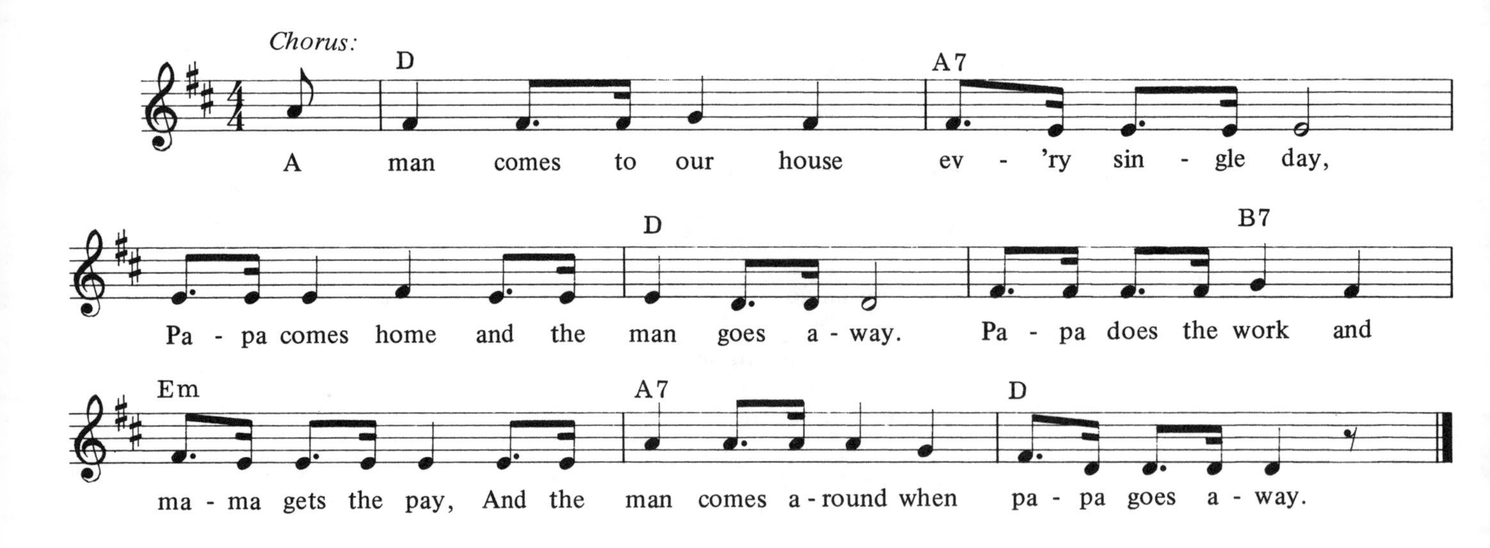
Chorus:
D
A7
A man comes to our house ev - 'ry sin - gle day,
D
B7
Pa - pa comes home and the man goes a - way. Pa - pa does the work and
Em
A7
D
ma - ma gets the pay, And the man comes a - round when pa - pa goes a - way.

D A7
The man who comes to our house, mama thinks is nice,
D
He comes in the summer and he brings mama ice.
B7 Em
Just a teeny-weeny bit that soon melts away,
A7 D
So he comes back once again later in the day. *Chorus*

D A7
The man who comes to our house drives a Cadillac,
D
He drives it 'round the block and he parks it in the back.
B7 Em
Mama rushes to the door, he's right there to greet her
A7 D
With, "Open up, honey, and let me check your meter." *Chorus*

D A7
The man who comes to our house isn't such a dope.
D
He climbs up on the porch with "I hope, I hope, I hope."
B7 Em
You can tell that he's a salesman by the way he slips inside.
A7 D
He never sells a thing but he comes out satisfied. *Chorus*

D A7
The man who comes to our house, comes to sell a brush,
D
He comes in a hurry and goes out in a rush.
B7 Em
After he is gone ma puts up an awful fret,
A7 D
If she doesn't get everything she thinks she ought to get. *Chorus*

```
      D                                      A7
The man who comes to our house, who comes to mow the lawn,
                                 D
Always seems to get here just when papa's gone.
              B7        Em
After he is gone my mother says to me,
      A7                                D
"You don't have to tell your pa everything you see." Chorus

     D                                  A7
The man who comes to our house to collect the trash
                                             D
Is tall, dark and handsome and he has a big moustache.
                 B7        Em
I'm not quite sure, and yet it seems to me
    A7                        D
That he's much nicer than a trashman ought to be. Chorus

      D                                    A7
The man who comes to our house comes to bring the milk,
                                                   D
He walks right in the kitchen and he talks as smooth as silk.
                      B7        Em
I always have to hold his horse out by the gate –
    A7                                     D
He stays so doggone long that the horse don't want to wait. Chorus

      D                                    A7
The man who comes to our house comes to fix the phone,
                                           D
He brings his tools along and he always comes alone.
                            B7    Em
Now just before he leaves, I think I ought to mention –
    A7                                      D
He rushes up to mama's room and fixes her extension. Chorus

         D             A7
Now, when I grow up I don't want to be
                                          D
A doctor or a lawyer – uh, uh, none of that for me.
                  B7                 Em
I don't want to have a great big office downtown –
 A7                     D
I just want to be the man that comes around. Chorus
```

THE MAN WHO FUCKED HIS HAT

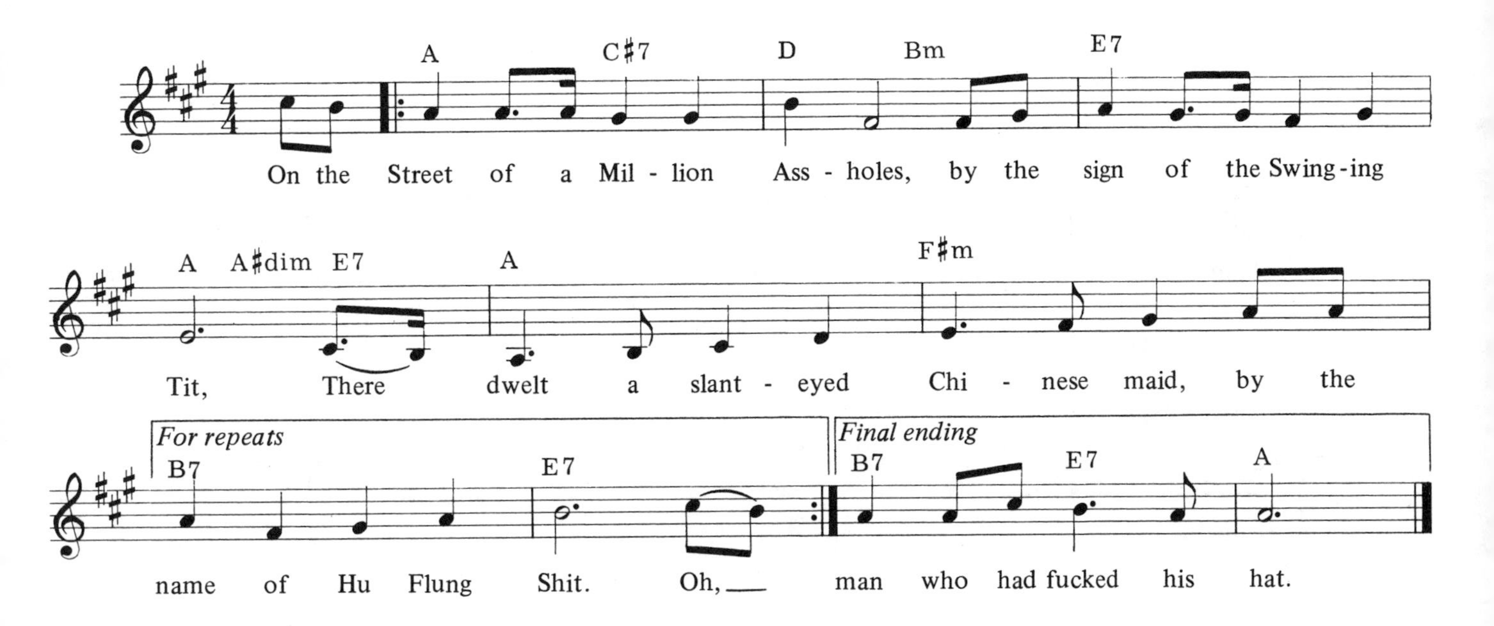
A C♯7 D Bm E7
On the Street of a Mil - lion Ass - holes, by the sign of the Swing-ing
A A♯dim E7 A F♯m
Tit, There dwelt a slant - eyed Chi - nese maid, by the
For repeats
B7 E7
name of Hu Flung Shit. Oh, —
Final ending
B7 E7 A
man who had fucked his hat.

A C♯7 D Bm
Oh, there she sat in the moonlight,
E7 A A♯dim E7
With a look of eternal bliss.
A F♯m
Oh, her tits were like two mountains,
B7 E7
And her eyes were pools of piss.

A C♯7 D Bm
Oh, she thought of her loves on the Bond Street,
E7 A A♯dim E7
And she thought of her loves long ago,
A F♯m
And she thought of the score she had laid on the floor,
B7 E7
When in walked Wun Hung Lo.

A C♯7 D Bm
"Oh, fly to my arms my bag of shit,"
E7 A A♯dim E7
He cried with dork in hand.
F♯m
"My love for thee will last as long as
B7 E7
Snow on the desert sand."

A C♯7 D Bm
Oh, gently she lowered her starboard tit,
E7 A A♯dim E7
And scratched her itchy prat.
A F♯m
Then looked at him with a half-assed grin,
B7 E7
And said, "Go fuck your hat! "

A C♯7 D Bm
Oh, his anger overcame him,
E7 A A♯dim E7
And he pissed upon the wall.
A F♯m
And he grabbed his hat and he fucked it,
B7 E7
And he trod on his one good ball.

A C♯7 D Bm
On the Street of a Million Sorrows,
E7 A A♯dim E7
By the sign of the Pregnant Cat,
A F♯m
They bore him away in splendor
B7 E7 A
As the man who had fucked his hat.

THE MARINES' HYMN

C
From the halls of Mon - te - zu - ma to the
G7
C
shores of Trip - o - li. We have fucked the
G7
C
whores on for - eign shores to prove our vi - ril - i - ty.
F
C
We have used pro kits and rub - ber tips just to
F
C C♯dim G7
tacet chords
C
keep our peck - ers clean. Still we have the high - est
G7
C
V. D. rate: We're U - nit - ed States Ma - rines.

MARY ANN

Tune: THE GIRL I LEFT BEHIND ME
D G
Oh, Mar - y Ann had a leg like a man, And a
D
great big hole in her stock - in', A chest like a drum and a
G A7 D
big fat bum, And a hole to shove your cock in. And
E7 A7
when you shove it in - to her she can - not keep from laugh - in', So,
D G A7 D
what do you say – let's go and play, And let me put my staff in.

D G
Oh, she jumped into bed and covered up her head,
D
And swore I could not find her.
G
But I knew damn' well she lied like hell,
A7 D
So I jumped right in behind her.

She shoved her feet right through the sheet
E7 A7
And showed her sausage grinder;
D G
So I rubbed my nuts against her guts
A7 D
And shoved it in behind her.

D G
Well, the wind it blew and the jizzum flew,
D
It flew right up her nightie.
G
And then I bit the nipple of her tit,
A7 G
Oh, Jesus Christ Almighty!

Well, I pumped her once and I pumped her twice,
E7 A7
And I pumped her once too often.
D G
Says she, "I'll die." "Don't cry," says I,
A7 D
"I'll lay you in your coffin."

THE MOUNTAIN BOY'S DREAM

G
D7
I strolled up to a whore-house and knocked up - on the door. My
G
knock was quick - ly an - swered by a half - dressed whore.

G D7
She asked me what I wanted, her feet were paved in brass.
G
I told her all I wanted was a little piece of ass.

G D7
I picked her up so gently and I carried her upstairs,
G
My hand slipped down a time or two among her golden hairs.

G D7
I was just about to come for my feelings were so grand,
G
When I woke up in my damned old bunk — a discharge in my hand.

MY NAME IS GONZALES

D
My name is Gon - za - les; I live in No - ga - les, I
work for a dol - lar a day. I
A7
go to see Nel - lie, I jump on her bel - ly, In
two min - utes she takes my dol - lar a - way.
D
Chorus:
She's a hot - blood - ed cock - suck - ing Mex - i - can whore.
A7
D

D
Oh, Nellie's a winner,
Each time I get in her,
A7
The two of us make such a fracas.
She's huffing and puffing,
I'm frantically stuffing;
D
My balls strike her ass with the sound of maracas. *Chorus*

D
And when I am on her,
There is no mañana –
A7
I don't give a damn for tomorrow.
She takes my last peso,
And if I may say so,
D
To fuck her once more I would beg, steal or borrow. *Chorus*

D
A Yankee turista
Was fucking my sister
A7
One night by the old hacienda.
She asked him for money,
He acted so funny,
D
He pulled up his pants and he said, "No comprenda." *Chorus*

D
When nine months had ended,
Her belly distended,
A7
The poor girl was really disastered.
As she went into labor,
She cursed that "Good Neighbor,"
D
Whose "Good Neighbor Policy" gave her a bastard. *Chorus*

MY NAME IS JOHN TAYLOR

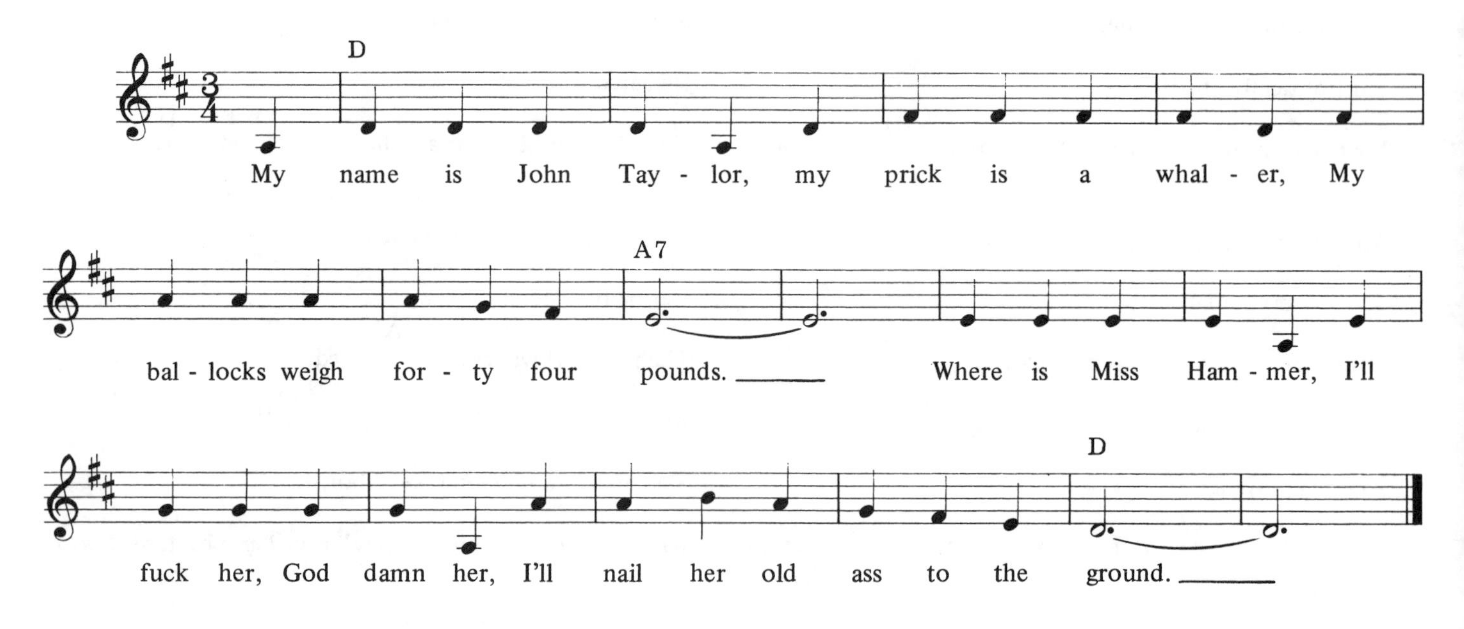
D
My name is John Tay - lor, my prick is a whal - er, My
A7
bal - locks weigh for - ty four pounds. ______ Where is Miss Ham - mer, I'll
D
fuck her, God damn her, I'll nail her old ass to the ground. ______

D
My name is Ben Croker, my tool is a poker,
A7
I strike while the iron is hot.

I love fornicating – it's so stimulating,
D
When I am surrounded by twat.

D
Ny name is Joe Tucker, I'm a motherfucker,
A7
The feeling is wonderfully grand.

When I am erected I'm never dejected,
D
May I put my prick in your hand?

D
My name is Maria, I've got gonorrhea,
A7
It itches like hell when I pee.

I got it by shagging, and though I'm not bragging,
D
Would you like to share it with me?

D
My name is Bob Becker, just look at my pecker,
A7
Did you ever see one so grand?

It quivers, it shivers, and when it delivers,
D
It whistles, "Let's Strike Up The Band."

D
I'm your friendly banker and I've got a chancre
A7
Right here on the end of my cock.

And when counting money it really is funny
D
To feel it drip into my sock.

D
In case of emergency or any urgency,
A7
Always remember the rule:

For jerking or fucking or simple cock-sucking,
D
You've got to take care of your tool.

MY SWEETHEART'S A MULE IN THE MINES

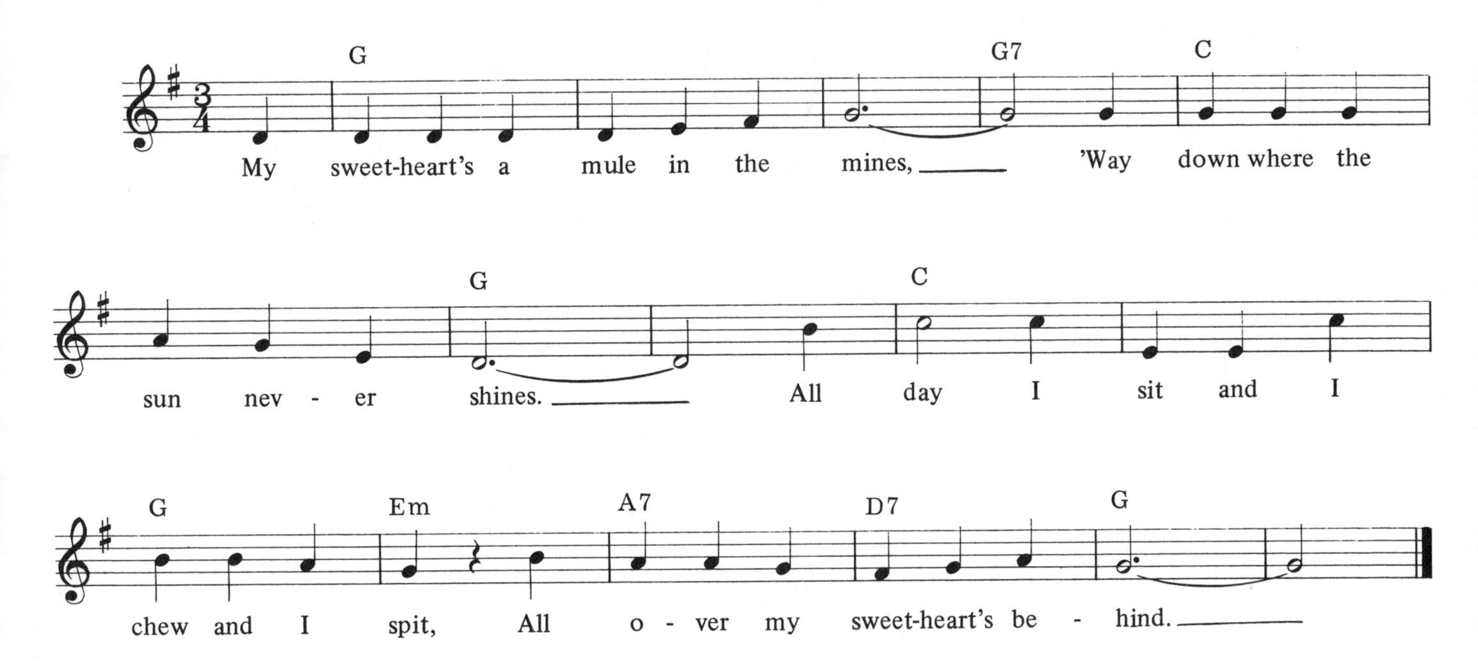
G
G7
C
My sweet-heart's a mule in the mines, 'Way down where the
G
C
sun nev - er shines. All day I sit and I
G
Em
A7
D7
G
chew and I spit, All o - ver my sweet-heart's be - hind.

MY SISTER MARY

This delightful song may be sung as a two, three or four-part round with the voices entering every two measures.

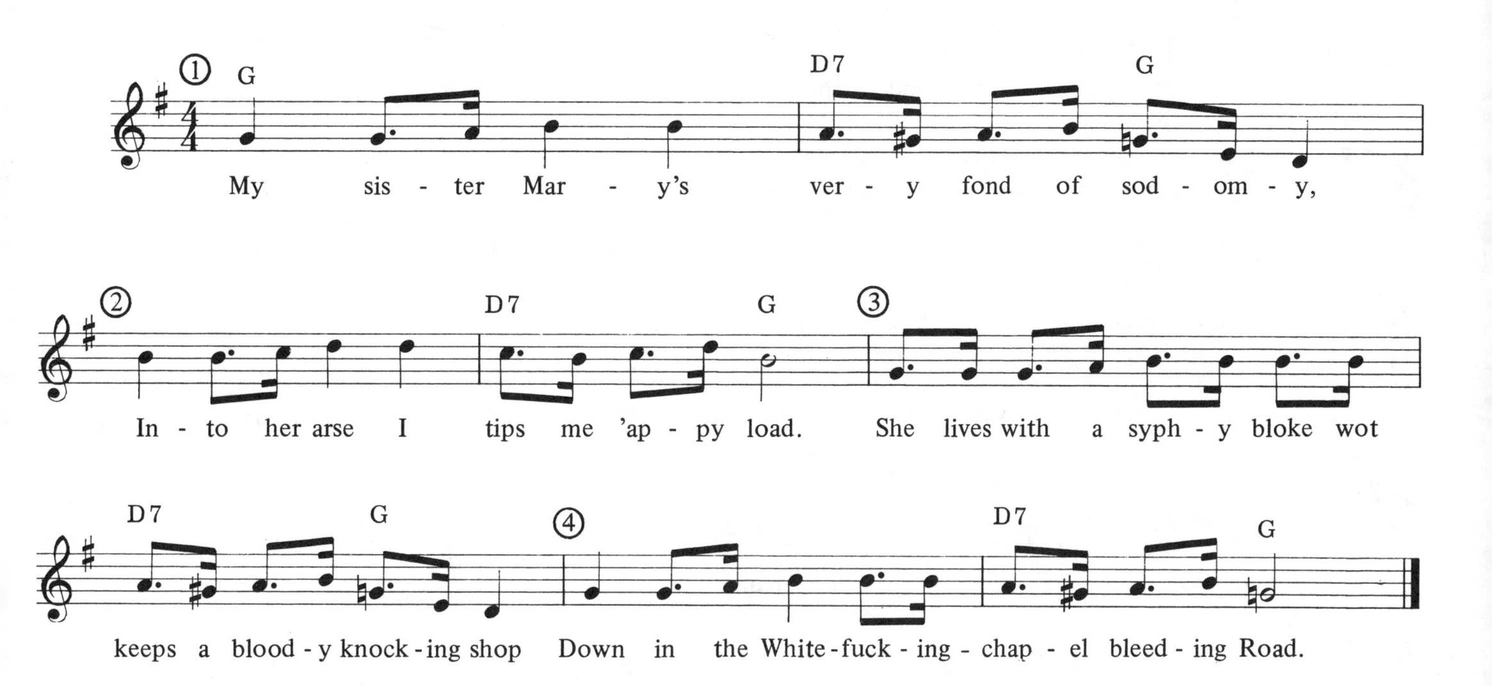
① G D7 G
My sis - ter Mar - y's ver - y fond of sod - om - y,
② D7 G ③
In - to her arse I tips me 'ap - py load. She lives with a syph - y bloke wot
D7 G ④ D7 G
keeps a blood - y knock - ing shop Down in the White - fuck - ing - chap - el bleed - ing Road.

NO BALLS AT ALL

Verse:
A D
Come all you good peo - ple, a sto - ry I'll tell, A
E7 A
song I will sing how a won - der be - fell A charm - ing young
D E7
maid - en who was wed in the fall, And mar - ried a man who had
A
no balls at all.
Chorus:
A D
No balls at all, Spoken (What?!) no balls at
E7 A
all, She mar - ried a man who had no balls at all.

A D
The night of the wedding she leaped into bed,
E7 A
Her breasts were a-heaving, her legs were a-spread.
D
She reached for his pecker – his pecker was small.
E7 A
She reached for his balls – he had no balls at all. *Chorus*

A D
"Oh mother, oh mother, oh, what shall I do?
E7 A
I've married a man who's unable to screw.
D
For many long years I've avoided the call,
E7 A
Now I've married a man who has no balls at all." *Chorus*

A D
"Oh daughter, oh daughter, now don't feel so sad,
E7 A
I had the same trouble with your dear old dad.
D
There are lots of young men who will answer the call
E7 A
Of the wife of a man who has no balls at all." *Chorus*

A D
Now the daughter she followed her mother's advice,
E7 A
And she found the proceedings exceedingly nice.
D
A bouncing young baby was born in the fall
E7 A
To the wife of the man who had no balls at all. *Chorus*

THE NORTH ATLANTIC SQUADRON

Chorus:
C G7 C
A - way, a - way with fife and drum, Here we come, full of rum.
Look - ing for wom - en who ped - dle their bum, In the
G7 C
North At - lan - tic Squad - ron.
Verse:
C
When we ar - rived in Mon - tre - al, She
G7 C
spread her legs from wall to wall. She took the Cap - tain
G7 C
balls and all in the North At - lan - tic Squad - ron.

C
We were seven days at sea,
G7 C
The Captain took to buggery.

His only joy was the cabin boy,
G7 C
In the North Atlantic Squadron. *Chorus*

C
A-sailing up and down the coast,
G7 C
Now, here's the thing we love the most:

To fuck the girls and drink a toast
G7 C
To the North Atlantic Squadron. *Chorus*

C
Well, off the coast of Labrador,
G7 C
We took on board a floating whore.

We fucked her forty times or more,
G7 C
In the North Atlantic Squadron. *Chorus*

C
A-sailing up to Newfoundland,
G7 C
Each sailor had his prick in his hand.

Oh say, my boys, can you make it stand?
G7 C
In the North Atlantic Squadron. *Chorus*

C
And when our ship is in drydock,
G7 C
The whores around us all do flock.

It's every man unfurl your cock,
G7 C
In the North Atlantic Squadron. *Chorus*

THE OLD CHISHOLM TRAIL

Old pioneers with great long ears,
They lived in fields and ditches.
They fucked their wives with Bowie knives –
The dirty sons-a-bitches. *Anon.*

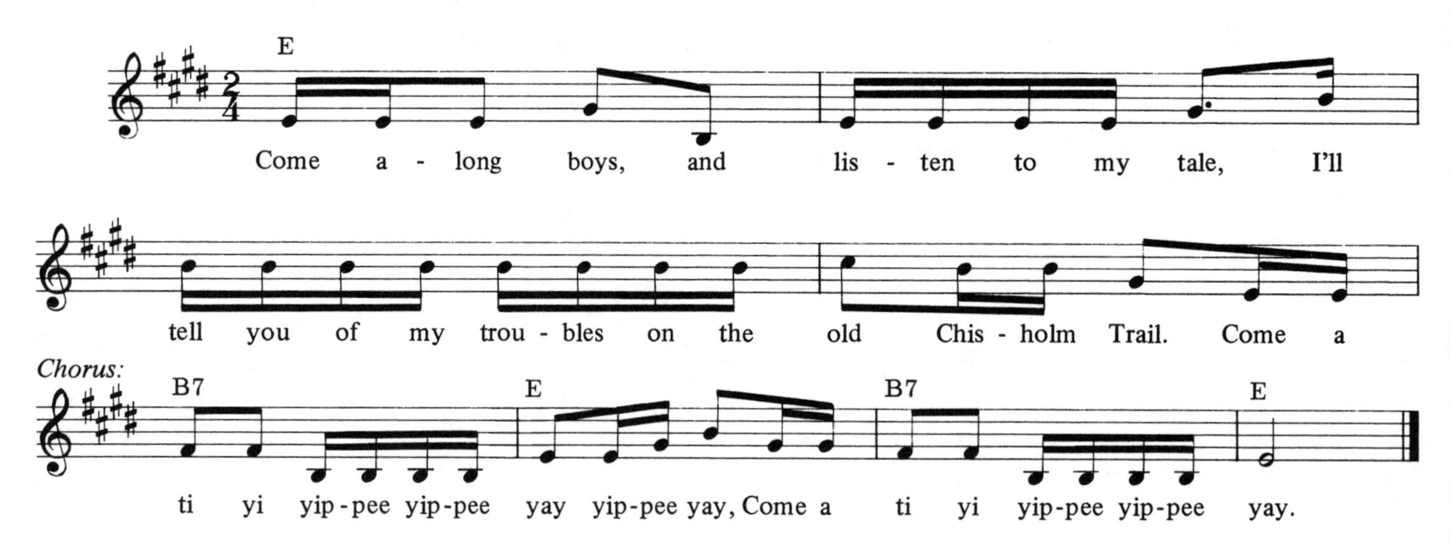

E
Come a - long boys, and lis - ten to my tale, I'll
tell you of my trou - bles on the old Chis - holm Trail. Come a
Chorus:
B7
E
B7
E
ti yi yip-pee yip-pee yay yip-pee yay, Come a ti yi yip-pee yip-pee yay.

E
With my foot in the stirrup and my ass in the saddle,
I gotta round up these sonofabitchin' cattle. *Chorus*

They sent me to the boss just to get a little roller,
I thought I'd go to town to get some tallow on my pole-a. *Chorus*

Oh, I rode and I rode and I rode to the south,
Till my horse's old tongue hung out of his mouth. *Chorus*

Now, little Fanny Walter was a nice fat squaw,
She lived down by the Chickasaw. *Chorus*

Well, when I met her I offered her a penny.
She said, "I am sorry but I haven't got any." *Chorus*

Well, when I met her I offered her a nickel.
She said, "I'm sorry but that wouldn't buy a trickle." *Chorus*

Well, when I met her I offered her a dime.
She said, "You'll have to try some other time." *Chorus*

Well, when I met her I offered her a quarter.
She said, "By God, I'm a cowpuncher's daughter." *Chorus*

Well, when I met her I offered her a half.
She said, "God dammit, I ain't no calf." *Chorus*

Well, I went to her house, laid a dollar in her hand.
She said, "Young man, can you make him stand?" *Chorus*

Oh, I took her by the waist and I throwed her down,
And my balls hit her ass before she touched the ground. *Chorus*

Well, I fucked her standing and I fucked her lying;
If I'd-a had wings I'd-a fucked her flying. *Chorus*

Well, when I got up she called me "kid."
She said, "You'll remember me," and by God, I did. *Chorus*

In about three days I began to feel sick,
And my underwear stuck to the end of my dick. *Chorus*

The very next day my prick turned blue,
I got so scared, didn't know what to do. *Chorus*

I went to the doctor with my cock in my hand,
Said, "By God, doctor, it's the worst in the land." *Chorus*

The Doc took a look and then said, "Cough."
I coughed so hard my balls fell off. *Chorus*

The doctor he rolled it with a little blue stone.
Says I, "Goddam you, doctor, let that alone." *Chorus*

Now every time I go out to pee,
Blood and corruption come from me. *Chorus*

And every time I go out to piss,
I think of the gal who gave me this. *Chorus*

The last time I seen her, and I ain't seen her since,
She was fucking a cowboy through a barbed-wire fence.* *Chorus*

The last time I seen her she was floating down the stream
With a handful of money and a belly full of cream. *Chorus*

So that's my story of my search for tail,
And I'm back punchin' cattle on the Old Chisholm Trail. *Chorus*

* Or, if you prefer:
She was scratching her cunt on a barbed-wire fence.
Ed.

"And your sister"

O MON BERGER FIDÈLE
O MY FAITHFUL SHEPHERD
French Medical Student song
Lyrically
D
A7
O mon ber - ger fi - dè - le, Viens t'en re - po - ser sur mon
O, my dear faith - ful shep - herd, O, come and re - pose on my
D
coeur.
breast.
A
And
A7
ma voix qui t'ap - pel - le, Viens t'en me don - ner du bo -
hear my voice that calls you, Then come and give me hap - pi -
D
heur.
ness.
Refrain: Rhythmically
D
A7
D
Ah! fous moi donc ta pine dans l'cul, Et qu'on en fi - nis - se.
Ah! shove your prick right up my ass, And let's get it o - ver.
A7
D
Ah! fous moi donc ta pine dans l'cul, Et qu'on n'en parl' plus.
Ah! shove your prick right up my ass. Bet - ter done than said.
D
Déjà tes testicules
A7 D
Battent sur mon pètard;
Voilà que tu m'encules,
A7 D
Je sens ton braquemard.
D
Your testicles already
A7 D
Are beating on my ass;
And now, 'way up my ass-hole,
A7 A
Your prick has made a pass.
Refrain
D
Ta langue me trifouille
A7 D
Plus haut que le gosier,
Et ton doigt me chatouille
A7 D
Plu bas que le gésier.
D
Your tongue has gone exploring
A7 D
Into my very throat,
And your finger now is boring
A7 D
Far down into my moat.
Refrain
127

ONE-BALL REILLY

Verse:
G
As I was sit - ting 'round the fire, get - ting drunk on
D7 G
gin and wa - ter, Sud - den - ly a thought oc - curred to me;
D7 Chorus: G 3
Why not shag O' - Reil - ly's daugh - ter? Fee fi fid - dle - ee i o,
D7 G
Rig a jig jig for the one ball Reil - ly, Rub it up, shove it up
C G D7 G
balls and all, Rig a jig jig, shag all.

G
I grabbed that she-bitch by the tits,
D7
Threw her down and nearly stove 'er.
G
Shag, shag, shag all night,
D7
She laughed like hell till the fun was over. *Chorus*

G
O'Reilly bursting through the door,
D7
Screaming screams of blood and slaughter,
G
Two horse pistols in his hands,
D7
To shoot the man who's shagging his daughter. *Chorus*

G
I grabbed that bastard by the neck,
D7
Stuck his head in a bucket of water.
G
Rammed those pistols up his ass,
D7
A damn sight further than I shagged his daughter. *Chorus*

G
As I go walking down the street,
D7
People shout from every quarter:
G
"There goes that God-damned son-of-a-bitch,
D7
The one that shagged O'Reilly's daughter." *Chorus*

PATRIOTIC SONG

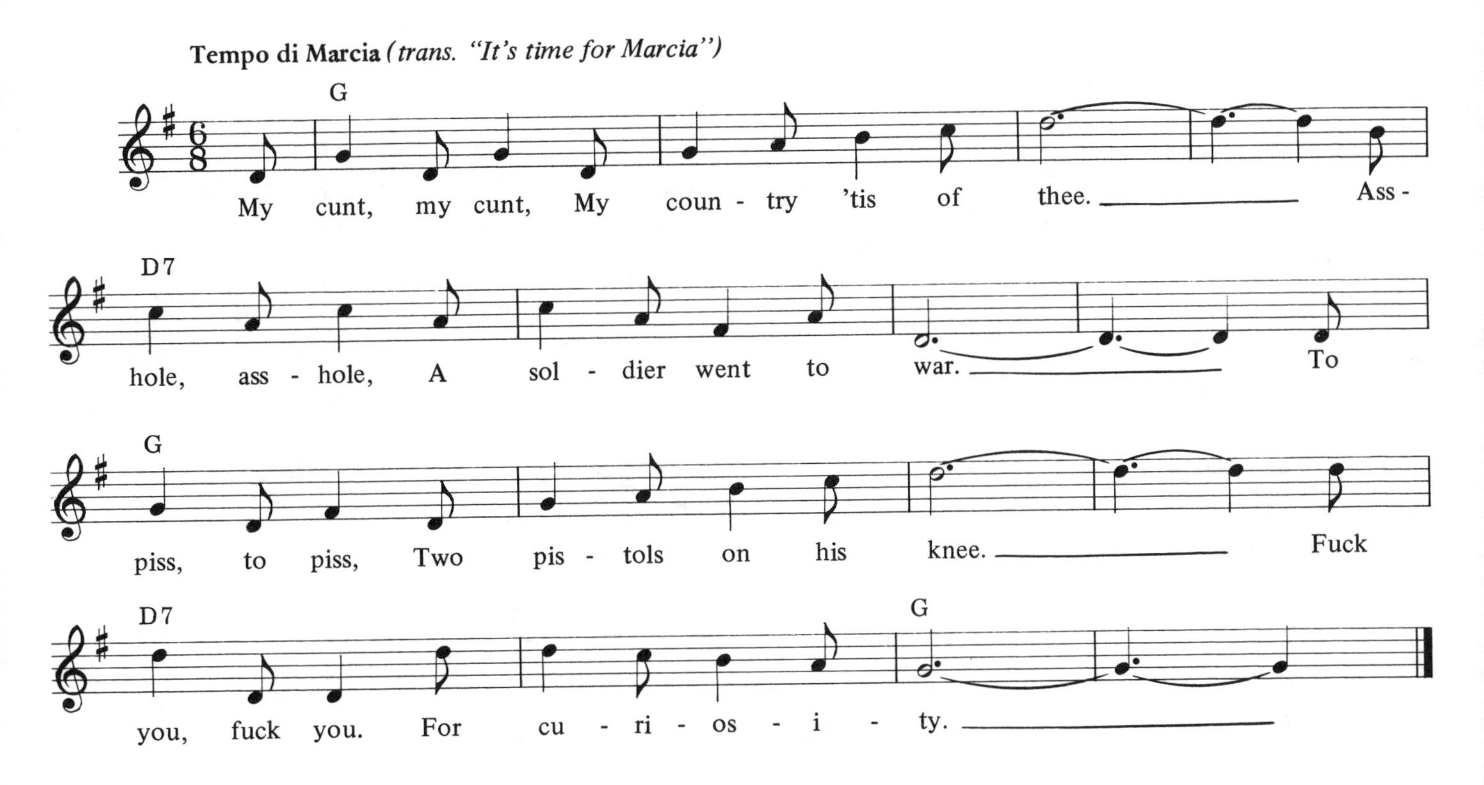
Tempo di Marcia (trans. "It's time for Marcia")
G
My cunt, my cunt, My coun - try 'tis of thee. Ass -
D7
hole, ass - hole, A sol - dier went to war. To
G
piss, to piss, Two pis - tols on his knee. Fuck
D7 G
you, fuck you. For cu - ri - os - i - ty.

PISSANYA, SHITANYA

A charming bit of pseudo-Russian nonsense. The two key words are related to the Russian words for "writing" and "sewing."

G D7
Pis - san - ya, Pis - san - ya, Pis - san - ya, Pis - san - ya's a
G C G
grand old name. If I had my way I'd Pis - san - ya all
E7 A7 D7 G
day. Pis - san - ya, Pis - san - ya, Pis - san - ya.
G D7
Shitanya, Shitanya, Shitanya,
G
Shitanya's a grand old name.
C G E7
If I had my way, I'd Shitanya all day.
A7 D7 G
Shitanya, Shitanya, Shitanya.

THE PORTIONS OF A WOMAN

G D
Now the por - tions of a wom - an that ap - peal to man's de - prav - i - ty are
C G D7 G Em
fash - ioned with the most ex - quis - ite care. And what may seem to you to be a
D A7
sim - ple lit - tle cav - i - ty, is real - ly an e - lab - o - rate af -
D C G
fair. Now, we doc - tors who have tak - en time to stud - y these phe - nom - e - na in
D7 G C C♯dim
num - bers of ex - per - i - men - tal dames, have made a lit - tle list of all these
G E7 A7 1. D D7 2. D7
fem - i - nine ab - dom - en - a, And giv - en them de - light - ful Lat - in names. There's the word: CUNT!
Spoken:

G
There's the vulva, the vagina
D
And the jolly perineum.
C G D7
And the hymen which is sometimes found in brides.
G Em
And lots of other gadgets,
D
You would love if you could see 'em,
A7 D
There's the clitoris, and Christ knows what besides.

C
Now it makes us rather tired
G
When you idle people chatter,
D7 G
About all the things to which we've just referred.
C C♯dim
And to hear you give a name
G E7
To such a complicated matter,
A7 D7
With such a short and unattractive word:

CUNT!

THE PLENIPOTENTIARY

CAPTAIN MORRIS, c. 1790

Em
The Bey of Al-giers, when a-fraid of his ears, A mes-sen-ger sent to our
B7
Am
court, sir, As he knew in our state the wom-en had weight, He
B7
Em
chose the one well hung for sport, sir. He searched the Di-van till he
D
found out a man Whose bol-locks were heav-y and hair-y, And he
Am
B7
Em
late-ly came o'er from the Bar-ba-ry shore As the great Plen-i-po-ten-ti-ar-y.

Em
When to England he came, with his prick in a flame,
B7
He showed it his Hostess on landing,
Am
Who spread its renown thro' all parts of the town,
B7 Em
As a pintle past all understanding.

So much there was said of its snout and its head,
D
That they called it the great Janissary;
Am
Not a lady could sleep till she got a sly peep
B7 Em
At the great Plenipotentiary.

Em
As he rode in his coach, how the whores did approach,
B7
And stared, as if stretched on a tenter;
Am
He drew every eye of the dames that passed by,
B7 Em
Like the sun to its wonderful centre.

As he passed thro' the town not a window was down,
D
And the maids hurried out to the area,
Am
The children cried, "Look, there's the man with the crook,
B7 Em
That's the great Plenpotentiary."

(continued)

Em
When he came to the Court, oh, what giggle and sport,
B7
Such squinting and squeezing to view him,
Am
What envy and spleen in the women were seen,
B7 Em
All happy and pleased to get to him.

They vowed from their hearts, if men of such parts
D
Were found on the coast of Barbary,
Am
'Tis a shame not to bring a whole guard for the King,
B7 Em
Like the great Plenipotentiary.

Em
The dames of intrigue formed their cunts in a league,
B7
To take him in turns like good folk, sir;
Am
The young misses' plan was to catch as catch can,
B7 Em
And all were resolved on a stroke, sir.

The cards to invite flew by thousands each night,
D
With bribes to the old secretary,
Am
And the famous Eclipse was not let for more leaps
B7 Em
Than the great Plenipotentiary.

Em
When his name was announced, how the women all bounced.
B7
And their blood hurried up to their faces;
Am
He made them all itch from navel to breech,
B7 Em
And their bubbies burst out all their laces;

There was such damnéd work to be fucked by the Turk,
D
That nothing their passion could vary;
Am
All the matrons fell sick for the Barbary prick
B7 Em
Of the great Plenipotentiary.

Em
A Duchess whose Duke made her ready to puke,
B7
With fumbling and fucking all night, sir,
Am
Being first for the prize, was so pleased with its size,
B7 Em
That she begged for to stroke its big snout, sir.

My stars! cried her Grace, its head's like a mace,
D
'Tis as high as the Corsican Fairy;
Am
I'll make up, please the pigs, for dry bobs and frigs,
B7 Em
With the great Plenipotentiary.

Em
And now to be bored by this Ottoman Lord
B7
Came a Virgin far gone in the wane, sir,
Am
She resolved for to try, tho' her cunt was so dry,
B7 Em
That she knew it must split like a cane, sir.

True it was as she spoke, it gave way at each stroke,
D
But oh, what a woeful quandary!
Am
With one terrible thrust her old piss-bladder burst
B7 Em
On the great Plenipotentiary.

Em
The next to be tried was an Alderman's Bride,
B7
With a cunt that would swallow a turtle,
Am
She had horned the dull brows of her worshipful spouse,
B7 Em
Till they sprouted like Venus's myrtle.

Thro' thick and thro' thin, bowel deep he dashed in,
D
Till her cunt frothed like cream in a diary,
Am
And expressed by loud farts she was strained in all parts
B7 Em
By the great Plenipotentiary.

Em
The next to be kissed, on the Plenipo's list,
B7
Was a delicate Maiden of Honor,
Am
She screamed at the sight of his prick, in a fright,
B7 Em
Tho' she'd had the whole palace upon her.

O Lord, she said, what a prick for a maid!
D
Do, pray, come look at it, Cary!
Am
But I *will* have one drive, if I'm ripped up alive,
B7 Em
By the great Plenipotentiary.

Em
Two sisters next came, Peg and Molly by name,
B7
Two ladies of very high breeding,
Am
Resolved one should try, while the other stood by
B7 Em
And watch the amusing proceeding.

Peg swore by the gods that the Mussulman's cods
D
Were as big as both buttocks of Mary;
Am
Molly cried with a grunt, he has ruined my cunt
B7 Em
With his great Plenipotentiary.

Em
The next for this plan was an old Haridan,
B7
Who had swallowed huge pricks from each nation,
Am
With over much use she had broken the sluice
B7 Em
'Twixt her cunt and its lower relation.

But he stuck her so full that she roared like a bull,
D
Crying out she was bursting and weary,
Am
So tight was she stuck by this wonderful fuck
B7 Em
Of the great Plenipotentiary.

Em
The next for a shag came the new Yankee flag;
B7
Tho' lanky and scraggy in figure,
Am
She was fond of the quid, for she had been well rid
B7 Em
From Washington down to a nigger.

Oh my! such a size! I guess it's first prize,
D
It's a wonder , quite next Ni-a-gary;
Am
W-a-l-l, now I'm in luck, stranger, let's fuck,
B7 Em
Bully for the great Plenipotentiary.

Em
All heads were bewitched and longed to be stitched,
B7
Even babies would languish and linger,
Am
And the boarding-school Miss, as she sat down to piss,
B7 Em
Drew a Turk on the floor with her finger.

For fancied delight, they all clubbed for a shite,
D
To frig in the school necessary,
Am
And the Teachers from France fucked à la distance
B7 Em
With the great Plenipotentiary.

Em
Each sluice-cunted bawd, who'd been screwed abroad
B7
Till her premises gaped like a grave, sir,
Am
Found luck was so thick, she could feel the Turk's prick,
B7 Em
Tho' all others were lost in her cave, sir.

The nymphs of the stage did his ramrod engage,
D
Made him free of their gay seminary;
Am
And the Italian Signors opened all their back doors
B7 Em
To the great Plenipotentiary.

Em
Then of love's sweet reward, measured out by the yard,
B7
The Turk was most blest of mankind, sir,
Am
For his powerful dart went right home to the heart,
B7 Em
Whether stuck in before or behind, sir.

But no pencil can draw this great-pintled Bashaw,
D
Then let each cunt-loving contemporary,
Am
As cocks of the game, let's drink to the name
B7 Em
Of the great Plenipotentiary.

PRETTY REDWING

D G D
There once was an In - di - an maid, Who al - ways was a - fraid That
A7 D E7
some buck - a - roo would slip it up her slue As she lay sleep - ing the
A7 D G D
whole night through. She had an i - dea grand, And filled it up with sand, So
A7 D A7 D
no big buck in search of a fuck could reach the Prom - ised Land. Oh, the
G D A7
moon shines bright on pret - ty Red - wing. As she lay sleep - ing
D G
there came a creep - ing, A cow - boy qui - et - ly came
D A7 D
creep - ing, His heart a - leap - ing as he spied her.

D
Redwing sprang to life,
G D
Whipped out her Bowie knife.
A7 D
With two quick cuts she severed his nuts
E7 A7
And then she stabbed him in the guts.
D
The cowboy he did die,
G D
Beneath the prairie sky.
A7 D
He stretched his luck in search of a fuck,
A7 D
For Redwing was too sly.

```
           G                              D
Oh, the moon shines bright on pretty Redwing.
             A7                     D
As she lies snoring there hangs a warning:
         G                      D
The cowboy's balls are now adorning
             A7               D
Her tepee awning for all to see.
```

```
     D
But to her big surprise,
     G          D
Her belly began to rise.
      A7                         D
And out of her cunt came a little runt
       E7              A7
Who had a strange look in his eyes.
       D
Poor Redwing was distressed,
  G              D
Until the chief confessed.
        A7                       D
"You can't pull the wool o'er Sitting Bull –
      A7              D
At fucking I'm the best."
```

```
           G                              D
Oh, the moon shines bright on pretty Redwing.
                 A7                   D
Within her tepee the kid makes peepee.
                 G                 D
And poor Redwing constantly is sleepy
                 A7                D
As she makes yippee with Sitting Bull.
```

THE RED FLAG

The chorus is a complete *non sequitur.* It is a parody of a British socialist worker's song entitled, what else, *The Red Flag.* If you don't feel it fits here, don't sing it. I think it adds just the right touch of social significance to an otherwise disgusting song.

Tune: **Tannenbaum**

E B7 E
While walk-ing a-cross the rocks so bare, I saw a maid-en ly-ing there. And
B7 E
as she lay in sweet re-pose, A breath of wind blew up her clothes. A
B7 E
sail-or who was pass-ing by Lift-ed his hat and winked his eye. And
B7 E
then he saw, to his de-spair, She had the red flag fly-ing there.
Chorus:
E B7 E
The work-ing class can kiss my ass, I've got the fore-man's job at last, I'm
B7 E
off the job, I'm on the dole – You can shove the Red Flag up your hole.

```
E
The sailor would not be denied,
   B7                    E
He said, "By God, I'll slip inside!"

He stripped down to his underwear,
     B7               E
And soon his ass was shining bare.
                              B7
     The maiden she was not perturbed,
                         E
     Not in the slightest bit disturbed,

For come what may, full well she knew
     B7                E
The brave red flag would see her through. Chorus
```

```
         E
The sailor he was shivering,
         B7            E
His mighty prick was quivering,

But soon he knew he'd met his match,
      B7           E
He could not penetrate her snatch.
                             B7
     Try as he might his path was blocked.
                          E
     All he could do was fire half-cocked.

To quit the fray he did prepare,
      B7                 E
And leave the fucking red flag there. Chorus
```

E
The moral of this tale is plain,
B7 E
But pardon me if I explain:

In love or war – it matters not,
B7 E
You never, never waste a shot.
B7
The sailor's judgement was at fault.
E
To penetrate the maiden's vault

With red flag flying, let it pass –
B7 E
Just shove it up the maiden's ass. *Chorus*

PUT ON YOUR OLD GRAY BUSTLE

Tune: **PUT ON YOUR OLD GRAY BONNET**

C C7 F
Put on your old gray bus - tle, get your fan - ny in a
F♯dim C Am D7 G
hus - tle, For to - mor - row the rent falls ___ due. ___
G7 C E7 Am F F♯dim
___ Get your fan - ny mak - ing mon - ey while the bees are mak - ing
C G7 C Am D7 G7 C
hon - ey, If you can't get five get two. ___

C C7 F
Put on the old blue ointment to the crabs disappointment,
F♯dim C Am D7 G G7
And take a hotshot every other day.
C E7 Am F F♯dim C
O my God, how it itches but it kills those sons of bitches
G7 C Am D7 G7 C
In the good old fashioned way.

THE RED LIGHT SALOON

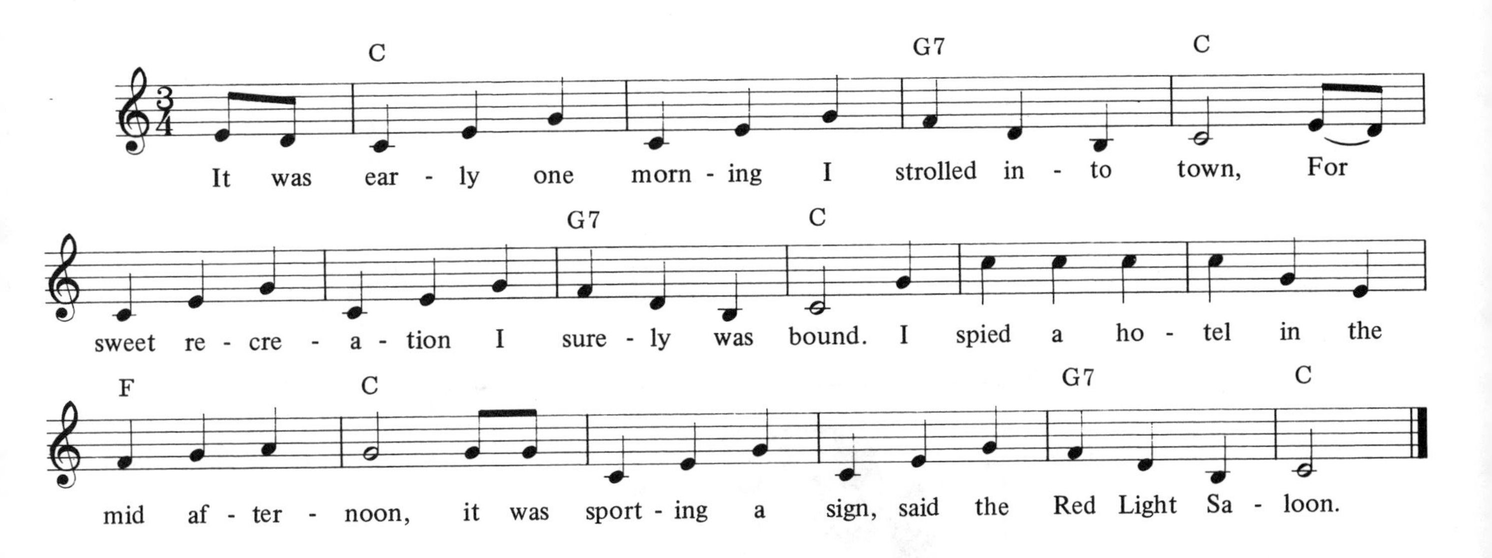
C G7 C
It was ear - ly one morn - ing I strolled in - to town, For
G7 C
sweet re - cre - a - tion I sure - ly was bound. I spied a ho - tel in the
F C G7 C
mid af - ter - noon, it was sport - ing a sign, said the Red Light Sa - loon.

C G7 C
I boldly walked in and strolled up to the bar.
G7 C
A pretty young damsel said, "Have a cigar."
F C
I took that cigar with all thanks for the boon,
G7 C
But she said, "That's our way in the Red Light Saloon."

C G7 C
Well, she mussed up my hair and sat down on my knee,
G7 C
Saying, "You are a lumberjack, that we can see.
F C
You are a lumberjack, that we all know –
G7 C
For your muscle is hard from your head to your toe."

C G7 C
She proceeded to feel if my muscle was right,
G7 C
And I smoked that cigar without striking a light.
F C
My head it was rising just like a balloon
G7 C
From the treatment I got at the Red Light Saloon.

C G7 C
Early next morning I bid her goodbye.
G7 C
She waved from the door with a tear in her eye.
F C
And I did not discover till sometime next June
G7 C
That she'd given me a keepsake from the Red Light Saloon.

C G7 C
Well, I cursed that young woman till the forest turned blue.
G7 C
And with whisky and women I swore I was through.
F C
But I knew as I swore that I'd give my fortune
G7 C
Just to be back once more in the Red Light Saloon.

ROLL YOUR LEG OVER

C
D7
If all the young girls were like fish in the ocean, Then I'd be a
G7
Chorus:
C
whale and I'd show them the mo - tion. Oh, roll your leg o - ver, oh,
F
C
G7
C
roll your leg o - ver, Roll your leg o - ver the man in the moon.

C
If all the young girls were like fish in a pool,
D7 G7
I'd be a shark with a waterproof tool. *Chorus*

C
If all the young girls were like fish in the brookie,
D7 G7
I'd be a trout and I'd get me some nookie. *Chorus*

C
If all the young girls were like winds on the sea,
D7 G7
I'd be a sail and I'd have them blow me. *Chorus*

C
If all the young girls were like cows in the pasture,
D7 G7
I'd be a bull and I'd fill them with rapture. *Chorus*

C
If all the young girls were like mares in the stable,
D7 G7
I'd be a stallion and show them I'm able. *Chorus*

C
If all the young girls were like bricks in a pile,
D7 G7
I'd be a mason and lay them in style. *Chorus*

C
If all the young girls were like bells in a tower,
D7 G7
I'd be a clapper and bang them each hour. *Chorus*

C
If all the young girls were like bats in a steeple,
D7 G7
And I were a bat, there'd be more bats than people. *Chorus*

C
If all the young girls were like little red foxes,
D7 G7
And I were a hunter, I'd shoot up their boxes. *Chorus*

C
If all the young girls were like little white rabbits,
D7 G7
And I were a hare, I would teach them bad habits. *Chorus*

C
If all the young girls were like trees in the forest,
D7 G7
And I were a woodsman, I'd split their clitoris. *Chorus*

C
If all the young girls were like telephone poles,
D7 G7
I'd be a squirrel and stuff nuts in their holes. *Chorus*

C
If all the young girls were like diamonds and rubies,
D7 G7
I'd be a jeweler and polish their boobies. *Chorus*

C
If all the young girls were like coals in the stoker,
D7 G7
I'd be a fireman and shove in my poker. *Chorus*

C
I wish all the girls were like statues of Venus,
D7 G7
And I were equipped with a petrified penis. *Chorus*

THE RING-DANG-DOO

D
A7
When I was a lad in my teens, I met a gal from New Or - leans. She
D
had blonde hair and blue eyes too, And she let me ride on the ring - dang - doo.

Chorus: (same tune as verse)

D
Oh, the ring-a-rang-roo, now what is that?
A7
It's soft and round like a pussy cat.

It's got a hole in the middle and split in two,
D
And that's what they call the ring-dang-doo.

D
She took me down into her cellar,
A7
And said that I was a mighty fine feller.

She fed me wine and whiskey too.
D
She let me ride ring-dang-doo. *Chorus*

D
Her father came and angrily said,
A7
"You have lost your maidenhead.

Well, pack your bags and your Kotex too,
D
And make your living off your ring-dang-doo." *Chorus*

D
So she went off to be a whore,
A7
And hung this sign above her door:

"One dollar each and three for two
D
To take a crack at my ring-dang-doo." *Chorus*

D
They came by twos, they came by fours,
A7
Until at last they came in scores,

But she was glad when they were through
D
For they had ruined her ring-dang-doo. *Chorus*

D
Now along came Pete, the son-of-a-bitch.
A7
He had blue balls and the seven-year itch.

He had the clap and the syphilis too,
D
And he put them all in the ring-dang-doo. *Chorus*

D
And now she lies beneath the sod;
A7
Her soul, they say, is gone to God,

But down in Hell, when Satan's blue,
D
He takes whirl at her ring-dang-doo. *Chorus*

SALOME

Verse:
G D
Down our street we had a lit - tle par - ty, Ev - 'ry - one was
A7 D
oh so gay and heart - y. We all had beers, talk a - bout a treat,
A7 D7 G
In a booz - er down the street. There was old Un - cle Jim, he was
D
fair fucked up, We put him in the cel - lar with the old bull pup.
A7 D A7 D D7
Lit - tle Sun - ny Tim was try - ing to get it in, With his ass hole wink - ing at the
G Chorus: G D
moon - light. Oh, Sa - lo - me, Sa - lo - me, My old gal Sa - lo - me.
A7 D7
Stand - ing there with her ass hole bare, Wait - ing for some-one to put it there. And
G D
slide it and glide it right up her fuck - ing chute. She could
A7 D7 G
shoot, shit, fight, fuck, Wheel a bar - row, drive a truck, That's my gal Sa - lo - me.
G
Monday night she fucks like hell,
D
Tuesday night she has a spell.
A7 D
Wednesday night she takes it up her back,
A7 D7
Thursday night she takes it in the crack.
G
And Friday night she takes it up her nose,
D
In between her fingers and down between her toes.
A7 D A7 D
Saturday night she dishes out the clap –
D7 G
And she goes to church on Sunday. Chorus

SAMUEL HALL

D A7 D
Oh, my name is Sam - uel Hall, Sam - uel Hall.
A7 D
My name is Sam - uel Hall, Sam - uel Hall.
G D
Oh, my name is Sam - uel Hall, And I've on - ly got one
A7 D
ball. But it's bet - ter than none at all. Fuck 'em all.

```
         D                       A7        D
Oh, I killed a man they said, so they said.
                             A7          D
I killed a man they said, so they said.
    G
I killed a man they said.
              D
Christ, I bashed his bloody head
       A7                                    D
And I left him there for dead. Fuck 'em all.
```

```
             D                         A7       D
Oh, they say that I must die, I must die,
                             A7          D
They say that I must die, I must die.
        G
They say that I must die,
                   D
And they'll hang me up so high.
           A7                                  D
Then I'll piss right in their eye. Fuck 'em all.
```

```
                 D                        A7        D
Oh, the parson, he will come, he will come.
                                 A7         D
The parson, he will come, he will come.
         G
The parson, he will come
                  D
With his tales of Kingdom Come.
              A7                                    D
He can shove them up his bum. Fuck 'em all.
```

```
                 D                        A7          D
Oh, the sheriff will come too, will come too.
                                A7            D
The sheriff will come too, will come too.
          G
The sheriff will come too,
                    D
With his motherfucking crew.
                A7                                 D
They've got fuck all else to do. Fuck 'em all.
```

```
           D                    A7        D
I see Molly in the crowd, in the crowd.
                                A7        D
I see Molly in the crowd, in the crowd.
           G
I see Molly in the crowd,
           D
And I feel so God-damned proud,
           A7                              D
That I want to shout out loud, "Fuck 'em all."
```

SAN MARQUEÑA

Mexico

Am
E7
San Mar - cos tie - ne la fa - ma ___ de las mu - je - res bo -
Am
E7
ni - tas. ___ San Mar - cos tie - ne la fa - ma, ___ de
Am
A7
las mu - je - res bo - ni - tas. ___ A - ca - pul - co tam - bién
Dm
Am
Chorus:
tie - ne, ___ Pe - ro no son se - ñor - i - tas. ___ San Mar -
E7
Am
E7
Am
que - ña de mi vi - da, ___ San Mar - que - ña de mia - mor.

San Marcos is famous
For its pretty women. } 2
Acapulco also has them
But they are not señoritas (i.e., not virgins)

Chorus: San Marqueña, my life,
San Marqueña, my love ("San Marqueña" is a woman from San Marcos, a Mexican city.)

Am E7 En la punta de la Quebrada Am Estaba cantando un gringo. } 2 A7 Dm En sus cantares decía Am "Si me caigo aquí me chingo." *Chorus*	*On top of the Quebrada (famous Acapulco cliff)* *A "gringo" was singing* *And in his songs he said,* *If I fall I screw myself."*
Am E7 Si tienes hijas solteras, Am Y todas son disolutas, } 2 A7 Dm Eres pobre porque quieres Am Pon una casa de putas. *Chorus:*	*If you have single daughters,* *And they are libertines,* *You do not have to be poor,* *Open up a brothel.*

continued

Am E7
Sal si es que vas a salir,
Am
Si no vas a salir ni salgas; } 2
A7 Dm
Pero si vas a venir,
Am
Te lavas muy bien las nalgas. *Chorus*

Get out if you are going out,
If you are not going out don't go;
But if you are going to come
Wash your ass well.
("Venir" has same significance as slang "come.")

Am E7
Cuando me pongo a cagar,
Am
Siempre me siento poeta, } 2
A7 Dm
O me da por dibujar,
Am
O tejerme una chaqueta. *Chorus*

When I begin to shit
I always feel like an artist, a poet.
Either I begin to draw,
Or I jerk off.
(Chaqueta means "jacket," but chaqueta is also jerking off. "Tejer" is "to knit" – so the double meaning: "I knit a jacket" vs. "I jerk off.")

Am E7
El autor de este volúmen
Am
Es un niño muy decente. } 2
A7 Dm
Solo un defecto tiene,
Am
Que le gusta el que está enfrente. *Chorus*

The author of this book
Is a decent boy.
He only has one defect
He likes the fellow that is facing him.
(i.e., he is a homosexual.)

Am E7
Una vieja y un viejito
Am
Jugaban al juego de Mata, } 2
A7 Dm
La vieja que se descuida,
Am
El viejo metió su reata. *Chorus*

An old man and an old woman
Were playing the game of Mata (a person's name)
The old woman gets distracted
And he introduced her his "cord."

Am E7
En el fondo del Rio Cual
Am
Hallaron al Señor Angulo. } 2
A7 Dm
No se sabe si murió ahogado
Am
O de un balazo en el culo. *Chorus*

On the bottom of the River Cual
They found Mr. Angulo.
It's not known if he died from drowning
Or from a bullet up his ass.

Am E7
Y en el centro de San Marcos
Am
Hay una banca bendita. } 2
A7 Dm
La señora que se sienta
Am
Amanece señorita. *Chorus*

In downtown San Marcos
There is a blessed bench
The señora that sits there
Wakes up a señorita.
(i.e., she regains her virginity.)

Am E7
Dame lo que yo te pido,
Am
Que no te pido la vida, } 2
A7 Dm
Del ombligo para 'bajo,
Am
De la rodilla pa 'rriba. *Chorus*

Give me my request,
I am not asking for your life,
Only from your belly button down
And from your knee cap up.

Am E7
Mujer que sale de noche
Am
Y en negro manto se enluta, } 2
A7 Dm
O puede que sea muy fea,
Am
O puede que sea muy puta. *Chorus*

A woman who comes out at night
Covered with black mourning shawl,
It is either because she is ugly,
Or because she is a whore.

Am E7
Y un pajarito volando
Am
Fué a meterse en un convento } 2
A7 Dm
Que alegres estan las monjas
Am
Con el pajarito adentro. *Chorus*

A flying bird
Entered a convent,
And the nuns are delighted
With the bird inside.
(In slang "pajaro" is the male organ.)

Am E7
Y un tiburón en la playa
Am
Le dijo a una ballena, } 2
A7 Dm
Si no me lo quieres dar,
Am
Retácatelo de arena. *Chorus*

A shark in the beach
Was telling to the whale,
If you don't want to give "it" to me,
Stuff it with sand.

Am E7
Y no me siento poeta,
Am
Ni en el aire las compongo, } 2
A7 Dm
Pero pásame a tu hermana,
Am
Y verás como la pongo. *Chorus*

And I don't feel like a poet
And can't make verses out of thin air.
But get me your sister,
And you'll see what happens to her.

Am E7
Como que quiere llover,
Am
Como que quiere hacer aire, } 2
A7 Dm
Y al que no le guste el canto
Am
Que vaya y chingue a su madre. *Chorus*

It seems as if it is going to rain
It seems as if it will be windy
And who doesn't like this song
Can go fuck his mother.

Contributed by Dr. Boris Rubenstein, formerly of Mexico City. *¡Muchas gracias!*

SHE ROLLED AND SHE TUMBLED

She's so tough she lays down among the nails and screws.
–Woody Guthre

Tune: **TURKEY IN THE STRAW**

E
Oh, her tits were swol - len and her ass was red, And she
F♯7 B7
sat there smil - ing on the edge of the bed. And I
E
said, "I'd like to fuck you," And she said, "You think you can?" So
B7 E Chorus:
then and there I jumped her and the ac - tion be - gan. Oh, she
rolled and she tum - bled and she shit on the floor, And she
A E
wiped her ass on the knob of the door, While the moon shone green on the
B7 E B7 E
nip - ple of her tit, And she brushed her teeth with a blue - bird's shit.

E
Well, this little girl really knew how to lay,
F♯7 B7
She was the best piece of ass that ever hit the hay.
E
The skin of her belly was as tight as a drum,
B7 E
And every time we fucked it went rum-a-tum-tum. *Chorus*

THE SEXUAL LIFE OF THE CAMEL

Chorus:
C G7 C F
The sex - u - al life of the cam - el is more than
G7 C G D7
an - y - one thinks. When the cam - el starts to get
G Em D7 G
pass - 'nate He tries to mount the Sphinx.
G7 C G7 C
But the Sphinx - 's ce - les - ti - al pas - sage is
G7 C G7 C F
blocked by the sands of the Nile, Which ac - counts for the hump on the
C G7 C G7 C
cam - el, And the Sphinx - 's in - scru - ta - ble smile.

C G7 C
When Lydia goes to pass water,
F G7 C
She pees an incredible stream.
G D7 G
She pees for an hour and a quarter,
Em D7 G G7
And you can't see her ass for the steam.

C G7 C
Which has nothing to do with the camel,
G7 C G7
Nor the Sphinx on that faraway shore,
C F C G7
But is merely a little diversion,
C G7 C
Till we all sing the chorus once more. *Chorus*

SHITHOUSE LAMENT

"Here I sit broken-hearted,
Paid a nickel and only farted." *(The pay-toilet blues)*

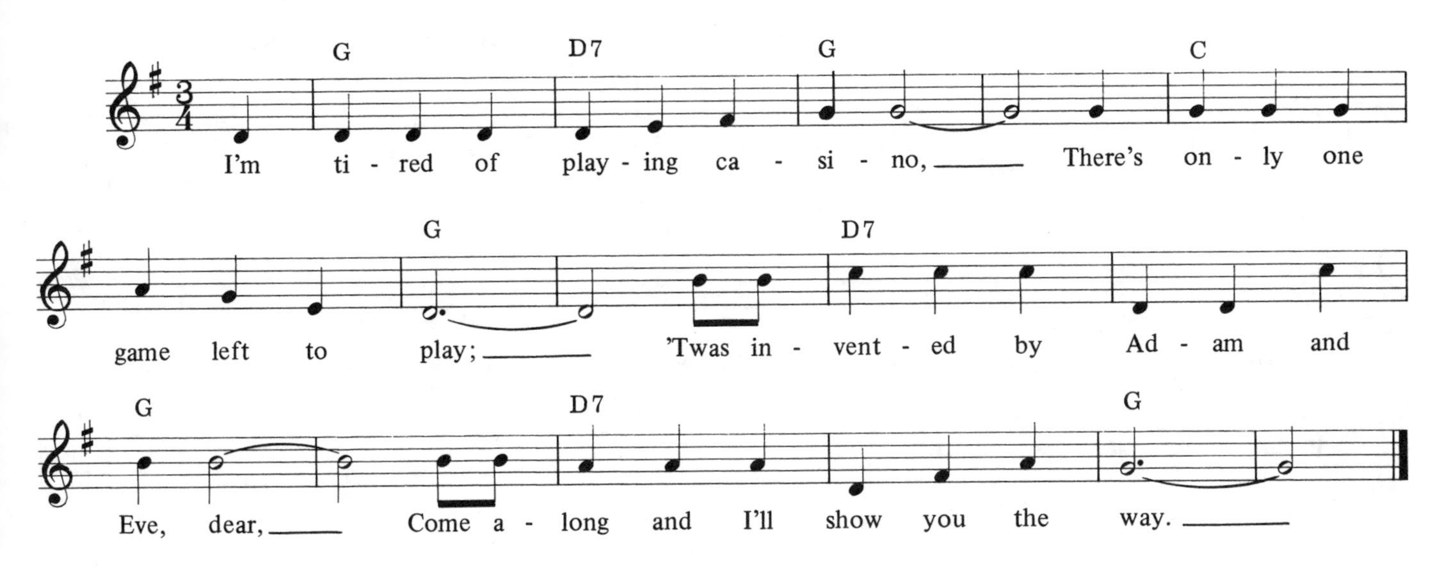
G D7 G C
I'm ti - red of play - ing ca - si - no, There's on - ly one
G D7
game left to play; 'Twas in - vent - ed by Ad - am and
G D7 G
Eve, dear, Come a - long and I'll show you the way.

G D7 G
I'll cover your fair face with kisses,
C G
Till it all seems like heaven, you'll see.
D7 G
I'll show you the bliss of all blisses,
D7 G
If you'll come to the shithouse with me.

G D7 G
Nine days have gone by, dear, forever.
C G
Oh God, how I wish I were dead.
D7 G
My body's all covered with itches,
D7 G
There's a pimple right on my prick head.

G D7 G
I've tried all the pills in creation,
C G
Way down to the tiny G. C.[1]
D7 G
I've suffered all hell and damnation
D7 G
Since you went to the shithouse with me.

G D7 G
Now, come along all you fair maidens,
C G
And likewise you chippies and whores,
D7 G
I'm going out into the country
D7 G
Where you'll not see my face any more.

G D7 G
As I ramble around the world over,
C G
A new thought has been born in my dome:
D7 G
With my cock in my hand in full blossom,
D7 G
I'll go to the shithouse alone.

[1]Probably an "anti-gonorrhea pill," since the gonococcus bacterium is referred to by the medical profession as "G.C."

SIX NIGHTS DRUNK

E
I came home the oth - er night as drunk as I could be, I
A E B7 E
saw a horse in the sta - ble where my horse ought to be, So I
said to my wife, my pret - ty lit - tle wife, now won't you tell me, please,
A E B7 E
What's this horse a - do - ing here where my horse ought to be. She said, "You
A E B7 E
darn fool, you drunk - en fool, can't you ev - er see? It's
A E B7 E
noth - ing but a milk cow my cous - in gave to me." Well, I've
trav-elled this wide world o - ver, ten thou - sand miles or more, But a
A E B7 E
sad - dle on a milk cow I nev - er seen be - fore.
E
I came home the second night,
As drunk as I could be,
A E
I saw a hat in the closet
B7 E
Where my hat ought to be.
So I said to my wife,
My pretty little wife,
"Now, won't you tell me please,
A E
What's this hat a-doing here
B7 E
Where my hat ought to be?"
A
She said, "You darn fool,
E
You drunken fool,
B7 E
Can't you never see?
A E
It's nothing but a bedpan
B7 E
My mother gave to me."
Well, I've traveled this wide world over,
Ten thousand miles or more.
A E
But a bedpan size seven-and-three-quarters
B7 E
I never seen before.

E
I came home the third night,

As drunk as I could be,
A E
I saw some pants a-hanging
B7 E
Where my pants ought to be.

So I said to my wife,

My pretty little wife,

"Now, won't you tell me please,
A E
What's these pants a-doing here
B7 E
Where my pants ought to be?"
A
She said, "You darn fool,

You drunken fool,
B7 E
Can't you never see?
A E
It's nothing but a tablecloth
B7 E
My uncle gave to me."

Well, I've traveled this wide world over,

Ten thousand miles or more,
A E
But a zipper in a tablecloth
B7 E
I never seen before.

E
I came home the fourth night,

As drunk as I could be,
A E
I saw a head on the pillow
B7 E
Where my head ought to be.

So I said to my wi fe,

My pretty little wife,

"Now, won't you tell me please,
A E
What's this head a-doing here,
B7 E
Where my head ought to be?"
A
She said, "You darn fool,

You drunken fool,
B7 E
Can't you never see?
A E
It's nothing but a melon
B7 E
My father gave to me."

Well, I've traveled this wide world over,

Ten thousand miles or more,
A E
But a moustache on a melon
B7 E
I never seen before.

(continued)

```
E
I came home the fifth night,

As drunk as I could be,
  A                E
I saw an ass on the mattress,
         B7                E
Where my ass ought to be.

So I said to my wife,

My pretty little wife,

"Now, won't you tell me please,
  A               E
What's this ass a-doing here,
        B7                E
Where my ass ought to be?"
                          A
      She said, "You darn fool,
              E
      You drunken fool,
        B7              E
      Can't you never see?
           A              E
      It's nothing but a pumpkin
            B7              E
      My sister sent to me."

Well, I've traveled this wide world over,

Ten thousand miles or more,
        A              E
But an ass hole on a pumpkin
  B7              E
I never seen before.
```

```
E
I came home the sixth night,

As drunk as I could be,
  A                  E
I saw a cock in the hole
         B7                  E
Where my cock ought to be.

So I said to my wife,

My pretty little wife,

Now, won't you tell me please,
  A                 E
What's this cock a-doing here,
        B7                   E
Where my cock ought to be?"
                          A
      She said, "You darn fool,
              E
      You drunken fool,
        B7              E
      Can't you never see?
           A              E
      It's nothing but a candle
            B7              E
      My brother gave to me."

Well, I've traveled this wide world over,

Ten thousand miles or more,
     A            E
But ballocks on a candle
  B7              E
I never seen before.
```

THE SOLDIER JUST FROM THE MARINE

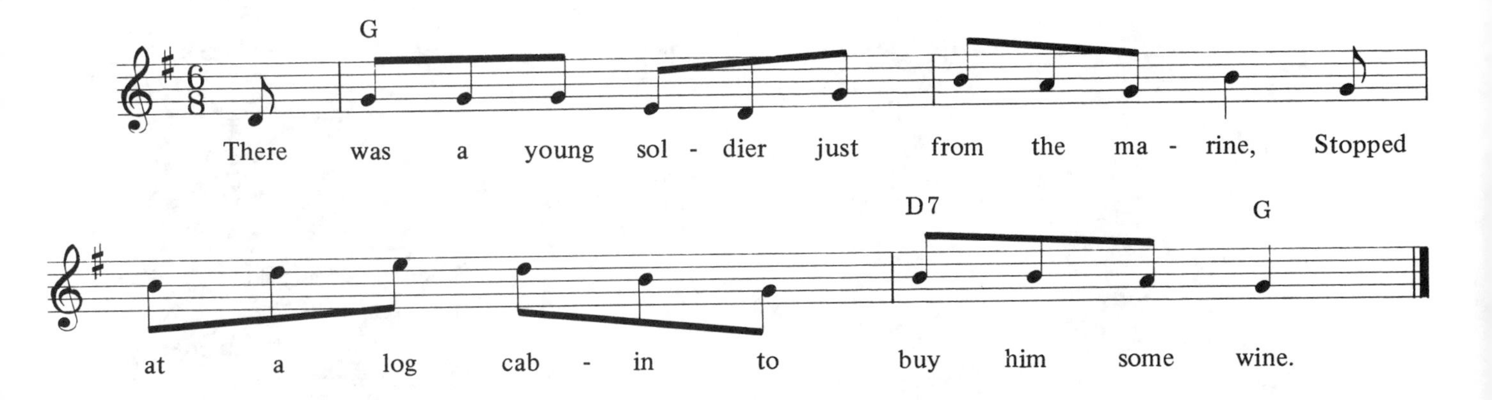
G
There was a young sol - dier just from the ma - rine, Stopped
D7 G
at a log cab - in to buy him some wine.

G
Oh lady, oh lady, your daughter's so fine,
D7 G
Please lend her to me for to have a good time.

G
Ah no, that cannot be, my daughter's too young,
D7 G
For hair on her cunt has just now begun.

G
Oh mother, oh mother, I am not too young,
D7 G
For I have been fucking the old blacksmith's son.

G
Oh daughter, oh daughter, if you're not too young,
D7 G
Just spraddle your legs out and let him crawl on.

G
Oh mother, oh mother, he's up on me now.
D7 G
A-hunching and punching like a bull on a cow.

G
Oh mother, oh mother, he's ruint me forever,
D7 G
He's bunged up my ass hole and busted my liver.

G
Oh daughter, oh daughter, you are such a fool,
D7 G
To let a man fuck you with a prick like a mule.

SUZANNE

G
D7
Su - zanne was a girl who had plen - ty of class, Who
1. For Repeats
2. Final Ending
G
knocked them all dead when she wig - gled her zanne was no Bore!
G D7
Eyes at the fellows as girls sometimes do
To make it quite plain that she wanted to
G D7
Take in a movie or go for a sail,
And then hurry home for a nice piece of
G D7
Ice cream and cake or a slice of roast duck,
For after each meal she is ready to
G D7
Go for a ride or a stroll on the dock
With any young man with a sizeable
G D7
Bank roll of bills and a pretty good front,
And if he talked fast she would show him her
G D7
Little pet dog who was subject to fits,
And maybe she'd let him take hold of her
G D7
Little white hands, with a movement so quick,
She'd reach right on over and tickle his
G D7
Chin while she showed him a trick learned in France
And asked the poor fellow to take off his
G D7
Coat while she sang an old song of the Mandalay Shore –
For whatever she was, Suzanne was no
G
Bore!

TAKE YOUR FINGERS OFF IT

Touchingly
C
Take your fin - gers off it, and don't you dare touch it, You
D7 G7 C
know it don't be - long to you. Take your fin - gers off it, and
A7 D7
don't you dare touch it, You know it don't be - long to you.
G7 C C7
You know it's sad to see a wom - an; an ex - tra good 'n'
F F♯dim C
Hold - in' back on her su - gar pud-din'. Take your fin - gers off it, and
A7 D7 G7 C
don't you dare touch it, You know it don't be - long to you.

```
C
Take your fingers off it, and don't you dare touch it,
    D7            G7      C
You know it don't belong to you.
                                            A7
Take your fingers off it, and don't you dare touch it,
    D7                   G7
You know it don't belong to you.
      C          C7
   Two old maids a-laying in bed,
     F                      F♯dim
   One turned toward the other and said,
 C                                A7
Take your fingers off it, and don't you dare touch it,
    D7            G7      C
You know it don't belong to you.
```

```
C
Take your fingers off it, and don't you dare touch it,
    D7            G7      C
You know it don't belong to you.
                                            A7
Take your fingers off it, and don't you dare touch it,
     D7                   G7
You know it don't belong to you.
         C              C7
   A nickel is a nickel, a dime is a dime,
       F                  F♯dim
   A house full of children, none of them's mine.
C                                  A7
Take your fingers off it, and don't you dare touch it,
    D7            G7      C
You know it don't belong to you.
```

C
Take your fingers off it, and don't you dare touch it,
D7 G7 C
You know it don't belong to you.
A7
Take your fingers off it, and don't you dare touch it,
D7 G7
You know it don't belong to you.
C C7
I may be little and I may be thin,
F F♯dim
But I'm an awfully good daddy for the shape I'm in.
C A7
Take your fingers off it, and don't you dare touch it,
D7 G7 C
You know it don't belong to you.

C
Take your fingers off it, and don't you dare touch it,
D7 G7 C
You know it don't belong to you.
A7
Take your fingers off it, and don't you dare touch it,
D7 G7
You know it don't belong to you.
C C7
I never been to heaven, but I been told
F F♯dim
Saint Peter taught the angels how to jelly roll.
C A7
Take your fingers off it, and don't you dare touch it,
D7 G7 C
You know it don't belong to you.

C
Take your fingers off it, and don't you dare touch it,
D7 G7 C
You know it don't belong to you.
A7
Take your fingers off it, and don't you dare touch it,
D7 G7
You know it don't belong to you.
C C7
Big fish, little fish swimming in the water,
F F♯dim
Come back here, man and marry my daughter.
C A7
Take your fingers off it, and don't you dare touch it,
D7 G7 C
You know it don't belong to you.

C
Take your fingers off it, and don't you dare touch it,
D7 G7 C
You know it don't belong to you.
A7
Take your fingers off it, and don't you dare touch it,
D7 G7
You know it don't belong to you.
C C7
There's just one thing I could never understand:
F F♯dim
Why a bow-legged woman likes a knock-kneed man.
C A7
Take your fingers off it, and don't you dare touch it,
D7 G7 C
You know it don't belong to you.

THERE WAS AN OLD FARMER

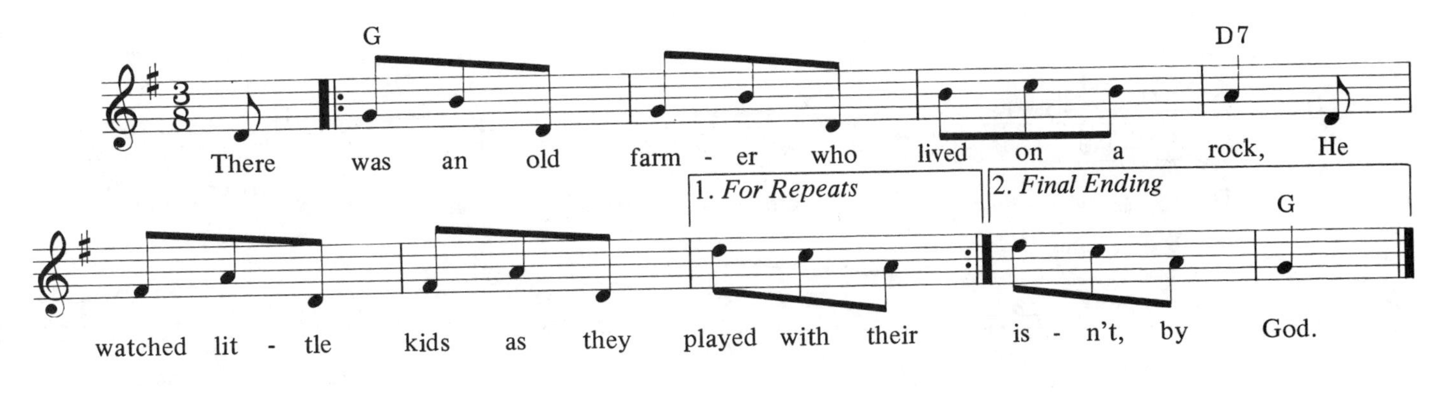
G
D7
There was an old farm - er who lived on a rock, He
1. For Repeats
2. Final Ending
G
watched lit - tle kids as they played with their
is - n't, by God.

G D7
Marbles and toys as in the days of yore,

And for a companion he had a young

G D7
Maiden, who laid down right there on the grass,

Who said she would show him the shape of her

G D7
Shoes and her stockings that fit like a duck.

She claimed she was learning a new way to

G D7
Bring up her children and teach them to knit,

While the boys in the barnyard were shovelling

G D7
Hay from the stables and filling the rick,

He said he would show her the length of his

G D7
Rowboats and oars, while approaching the falls,

And while going over he injured his

G D7
Long middle finger, which pained him a lot.

To soothe it he stuck it right into her

G D7
Hand me my rifle, I'm going to hunt,

And while I am gone take good care of your

G D7
Little pet rabbits that roam o'er the sod.

G
You think this is bullshit – but it isn't, by God!

THE TROOPER

G
D
There was an old wom - an lived un - der a hill,
G
D
Lol - ly lol - ly lol - ly - lo, She had good beer and
C
G
D7
G
ale for to sell. Lol - ly lo lol - ly lo, lol - ly lol - ly lol - ly lo.

G D
She had a daughter, her name was Sis.
G
Lolly lolly lolly lo.
D C
She kept her at home for to welcome her guests.
G D7 G
Lolly lo lolly lo, lolly lolly lolly lo.

G D
There came a trooper riding by.
G
Lolly lolly lolly lo.
D C
He called for drink so plentifully.
G D7 G
Lolly lo lolly lo, lolly lolly lolly lo.

G D
When one pot was out he called for another.
G
Lolly lolly lolly lo.
D C
He kissed the daughter before the mother.
G D7
Lolly lo lolly lo, lolly lolly lolly lo.

G D
When night came on, to bed they went.
G
Lolly lolly lolly lo.
D C
It was with the mother's own consent.
G D7 G
Lolly lo lolly lo, lolly lolly lolly lo.

G D
Quoth she, "What is this so stiff and warm?"
G
Lolly lolly lolly lo.
D C
"'Tis Ball, my nag, he will do you no harm."
G D7 G
Lolly lo lolly lo, lolly lolly lolly lo.

G D
"But what is this hangs under his chin?"
G
Lolly lolly lolly lo.
D C
"'Tis the bag he puts his provender in."
G D7 G
Lolly lo lolly lo, lolly lolly lolly lo.

```
          G                                              D
Quoth he, "What is this? " Quoth she, " 'Tis a well,"

      Lolly lolly lolly lo.
        D                      C
"Where Ball, your nag can drink his fill."
          G                D7      G
      Lolly lo lolly lo, lolly lolly lolly lo.

        G                                       D
"But what if my nag should chance to slip in?"
        G
      Lolly lolly lolly lo.
        D                          C
"Catch hold of the grass that grows on the brim."
          G                D7      G
      Lolly lo lolly lo, lolly lolly lolly lo.

        G                                     D
"But what if the grass should chance to fail?"
        G
      Lolly lolly lolly lo.
              D                             C
"Shove him in by the head, pull him out by the tail."
          G                D7      G
      Lolly lo lolly lo, lolly lolly lolly lo.
```

THE TINKER

Em G B7 Em
There was a jol - ly tin - ker, and he came from Dun - ga - ree, With a
C D G Am Em
Chorus:
yard and a half of fore - skin hang - ing down be - low his knee. With his
Em G B7 Em
long dong did - dly whack - er, O - ver - grown kid - ney crack - er
C D G Am Em C Em
Moth - er fuck - ing ba - by fetch - er hang - ing to his knees.

Em
My lady she was dressing,
G B7 Em
She was dressing for the ball,
C D G
When she saw the jolly tinker
Am Em
Lashing piss against the wall. *Chorus*

Em
"Oh tinker, oh, dear tinker,
G B7 Em
Oh, I'm in love with you.
C D G
Oh, tinker, oh, dear tinker,
Am Em
Will half a dollar do?" *Chorus*

Em
Oh, he screwed her in the parlor;
G B7 Em
He fucked her in the hall,
C D G
And the servant said, "By Jesus,
Am Em
He'll be cramming on us all." *Chorus*

Em
There were fifty naked women
G B7 Em
Running up and down the hall,
C D G
Shouting, "Jesus Christ, Almighty,
Am Em
Is he gonna fuck us all?" *Chorus*

Em
"Oh, daughter, oh, my daughter,
G B7 Em
You were a silly fool,
C D G
To get busy with a man
Am Em
With a tool like a mule." *Chorus*

Em
Oh, mother, oh, dear mother,
G B7 Em
I thought I was able,
C D G
But he split me up the belly
Am Em
From the cunt up to the navel." *Chorus*

Em
Said the mother to the daughter
G B7 Em
"Why you God-damned fucking whore!
C D G
If he gave you twenty inches,
Am Em
You would ask for twenty more." *Chorus*

Em
Oh, the tinker's dead and buried.
G B7 Em
I'll bet he's gone to Hell.
C D G
He said he'd fuck the Devil,
Am Em
And I'll bet he's done it well. *Chorus*

THEY'RE MOVING FATHER'S GRAVE TO BUILD A SEWER

To shit-house artists when they die,
We'll build it wide and build it high.
In tribute to their brain and wit,
A monument of solid shit.
Anon.

Movingly
G
D7
They're mov - ing fa - ther's grave to build a sew - er, They're
G
Em
mov - ing it re - gard - less of ex - pense. They're mov - ing his re - mains to
1.2.3.
A7
D7
To next verse
lay down shit-house drains, To sat - is - fy some near - by res - i - dents. 2. Now
Final Ending
Em
D7
G
had the blood - y nerve, To bug - ger up a Brit - ish work-man's grave.
(a work-man's grave.)

G D7
How, what's the use of having a religion;
G
For when you die your troubles never cease.
Em
When some high-society twit needs a pipeline for his shit,
A7 D7
They won't let poor old father rest in peace.

G D7
My father in his life was ne'er a quitter,
G
I'm sure that he'll not be a quitter now.
Em
He'll put on a white sheet and haunt that shithouse seat,
A7 D7
And he'll only let them shit when he'll allow.

G D7
Oh, won't there be some pains of constipation!
G
And won't those shithouse bastards rant and rave!
Em
But they'll get what they deserve, for they had the bloody nerve
D7 G
To bugger up a British workman's grave.

UNCLE FRED AND AUNTIE MABEL

Music by **FELIX MENDELSSOHN**
(Believe it or not!)

D A D A D Em D A7 D
Un - cle Fred and Aun - tie Ma - bel faint - ed at the break- fast ta - ble.
A D A E A E7 A
Would not heed the aw - ful warn - ing, "Not to try it ear - ly morn - ing."
D Em D A D Bm Em D A
Phil - o - scence soon put them right, To car - ry on the live - long night,
1. 2.
G B7 Em B7 Em A7 D Bm A7 F♯ Bm A7 D
Now, they're hop-ing ver - y soon to try it in the af - ter - noon. af - ter - noon.

D A D A
Uncle Fred and Auntie Mabel
D Em D A7 D
Find themselves extremely able.
A D A
Since they took that famed elixir,
E A E7 A
Freddie regularly sticks 'er.
D Em D A
After breakfast, during lunch,
D Bm Em D A
You can hear their bedsprings crunch.
G B7 Em B7 Em
Fred and Mabel both agree,
A7 D Bm A7 F♯
It hits the spot at half-past three.[1]
G B7 Em B7 Em
Fred and Mabel both agree,
A7 D Bm A7 D
It hits the spot at half-past three.

[1]Variant: It hits the spot right after tea.

THE WELSH MINER

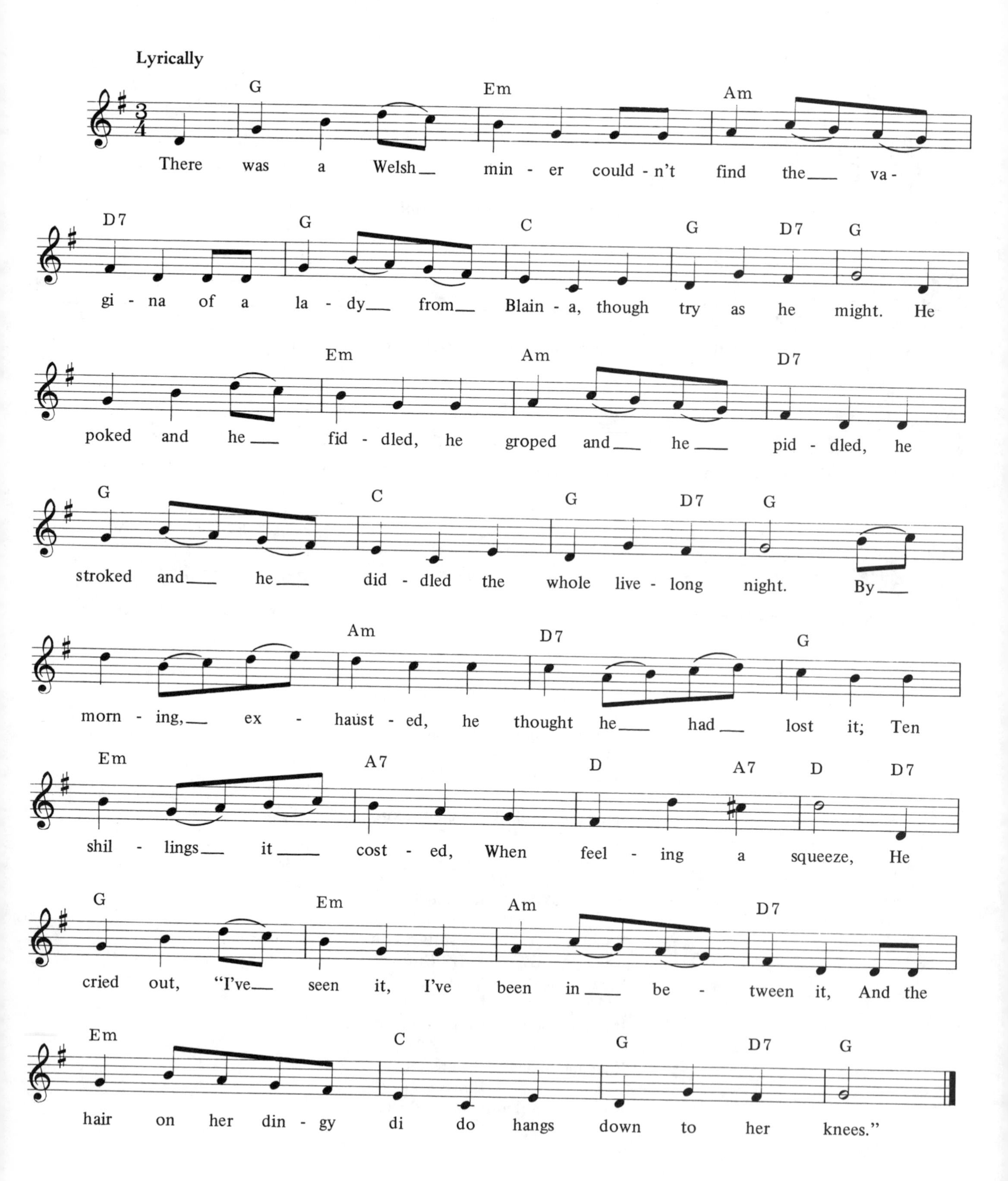
Lyrically
G Em Am
There was a Welsh_ min - er could - n't find the_ va -
D7 G C G D7 G
gi - na of a la - dy_ from_ Blain - a, though try as he might. He
Em Am D7
poked and he_ fid - dled, he groped and_ he_ pid - dled, he
G C G D7 G
stroked and_ he_ did - dled the whole live - long night. By_
Am D7 G
morn - ing,_ ex - haust - ed, he thought he_ had_ lost it; Ten
Em A7 D A7 D D7
shil - lings_ it_ cost - ed, When feel - ing a squeeze, He
G Em Am D7
cried out, "I've_ seen it, I've been in_ be - tween it, And the
Em C G D7 G
hair on her din - gy di do hangs down to her knees."

WHAT SHALL WE DO WITH THE DRUNKEN SAILOR?

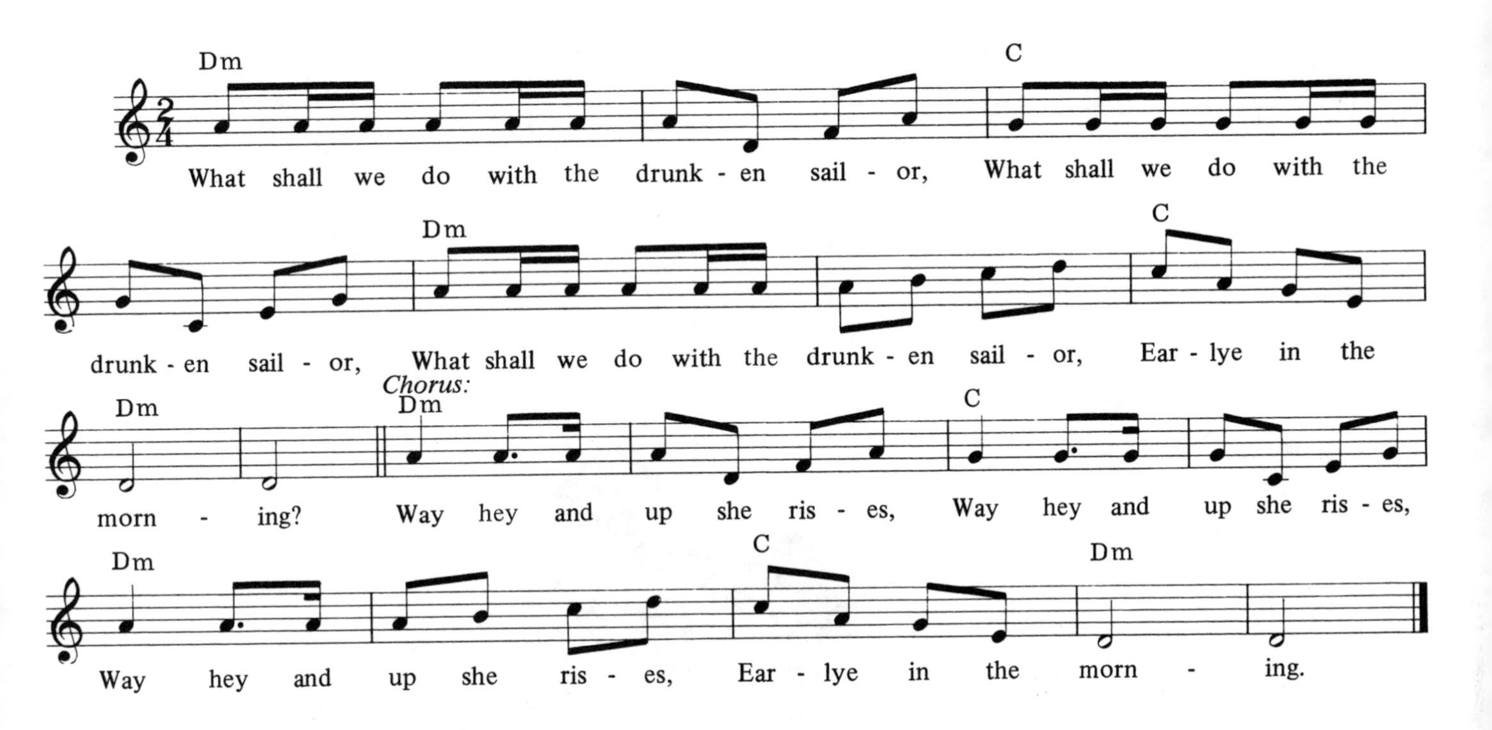

Dm
C
What shall we do with the drunk - en sail - or, What shall we do with the
Dm
C
drunk - en sail - or, What shall we do with the drunk - en sail - or, Ear - lye in the
Dm
Chorus:
Dm
C
morn - ing? Way hey and up she ris - es, Way hey and up she ris - es,
Dm
C
Dm
Way hey and up she ris - es, Ear - lye in the morn - ing.

Dm
Put him into bed with the captain's daughter,
C
Put him into bed with the captain's daughter,
Dm
Put him into bed with the captain's daughter,
C Dm
Earlye in the morning. *Chorus*

Dm
Hang him by the balls in a running bowline,
C
Hang him by the balls in a running bowline,
Dm
Hang him by the balls in a running bowline,
C Dm
Earlye in the morning. *Chorus*

Dm
Shave his crotch with a rusty razor,
C
Shave his crotch with a rusty razor,
Dm
Shave his crotch with a rusty razor,
C Dm
Earlye in the morning. *Chorus*

Dm
Shove a hose pipe up his ass hole,
C
Shove a hose pipe up his ass hole,
Dm
Shove a hose pipe up his ass hole,
C Dm
Earlye in the morning. *Chorus*

Dm
Tie his prick in a double half-hitch,
C
Tie his prick in a double half-hitch,
Dm
Tie his prick in a double half-hitch,
C Dm
Earlye in the morning. *Chorus*

Dm
That's what we'll do with the drunken sailor,
C
That's what we'll do with the drunken sailor,
Dm
That's what we'll do with the drunken sailor,
C Dm
Earlye in the morning. *Chorus*

THE WILD-WEST SHOW

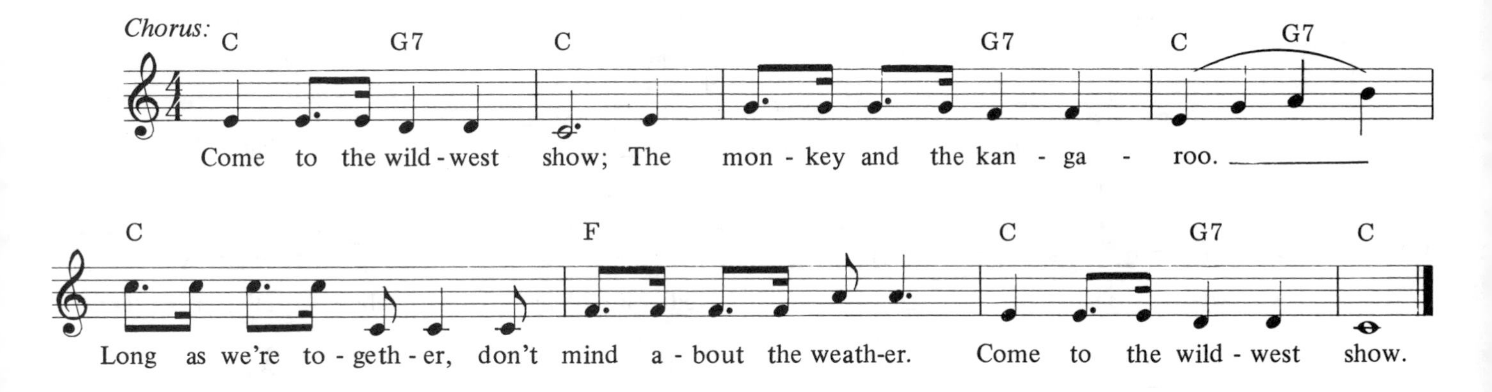
Chorus:
C G7 C G7 C G7
Come to the wild-west show; The mon-key and the kan-ga-roo.
C F C G7 C
Long as we're to-geth-er, don't mind a-bout the weath-er. Come to the wild-west show.

Spoken

Roll up, roll up! Come and see the wild man from Borneo, The only man in the world without a fundamental orifice. What's that, lady – how does he shit? He doesn't shit. That's what makes him so fucking wild. *Chorus*

Roll up, roll up! Come and see the leopard. A spot for every day of the year. Charlie, lift his tail and show the lady February the twenty-ninth. *Chorus*

Roll up, roll up! Come and see the armadillo. The tightest skinned animal in the world. Every time he winks he wanks. Now rapidly becoming extinct due to small boys throwing sand in his eyes. *Chorus*

Roll up, roll up! Come and see the elephant. The largest turds in the world. Every time he shits, he shits a ton. Charlie, bring the shovel. There's another little boy disappeared. *Chorus*

Roll up, roll up! Come and see the orang-utang. So named because of his two large testicles which bang together as he walks through the jungle – *orang-utang, orang-utang. . .Chorus*

Roll up, roll up! Come and see the goony bird. He flies in ever decreasing concentric circles until he disappears up his own fundamental orifice and fires gobs of shit at his baffled pursuers. *Chorus*

Roll up, roll up! Come and see the porcupine. His quills are razor sharp that no living creature dares approach him. What's that, lady – how does he fuck? Very carefully, very carefully. *Chorus*

ZULEIKA

Am E7 Dm
Zu - lei - ka was fair to see, A fair Per - sian
Am A7 Dm
maid - en was she. She lived in Bagh - dad, where all men are
Am E7 Am A7
bad, But none was so bad as she. She lived in Bagh -
Dm Dm6 Am E7 Am
dad, where all men were bad, But none was so bad as she.

Am E7
Her husband, he was very old,
Dm Am
With millions in silver and gold,
A7 Dm
He kept her locked in, away from all sin;
Am E7 Am
For Persians they are very bold.
A7 Dm Dm6
He kept her locked in, away from all sin;
Am E7 Am
For Persians they are very bold.

Am E7
On her head she wore a turban,
Dm Am
Which came from the looms of Iran.
A7 Dm
Where no one could see, she kept a small key,
Am E7 Am
Which she threw out again and again.
A7 Dm Dm6
Where no one could see, she kept a small key,
Am E7 Am
Which she threw out again and again.

Am E7
The first time she threw the key out,
Dm Am
It fell by the old water spout.
A7 Dm
She sighed and she cried as the door opened wide,
Am E7 Am
And in walked her lover, Mahout.
A7 Dm Dm6
She sighed and she cried as the door opened wide,
Am E7 Am
And in walked her lover Mahout.

Am E7
Mahout, he was known far and wide,
Dm Am
His prowess was his foremost pride.
A7 Dm
From servant to queen – betwixt and between,
Am E7 Am
His wonderful tool never shied.
A7 Dm Dm6
From servant to queen – betwixt and between,
Am E7 Am
His wonderful tool never shied.

Am E7
Zuleika did grasp him below,
Dm Am
Down there where the testicles grow.
A7 Dm
While giving a grunt, she offered her cunt,
Am E7 Am
And said, "Don't forget to come slow."
A7 Dm Dm6
While giving a grunt, she offered her cunt,
Am E7 Am
And said, "Don't forget to come slow."

Am E7
When brave Mahout's courage was spent,
Dm Am
Zuleika was hardly content.
A7 Dm
She said to him, "Love, when push comes to shove,
Am E7 Am
You'd better get back to your tent.
A7 Dm Dm6
She said to him, "Love, when push comes to shove,
Am E7 Am
You'd better get back to your tent.

Am E7
The next time she threw out her key,
Dm Am
It fell by the old banyan tree.
A7 Dm
She sighed and she cried as the door opened wide,
Am E7 Am
And in walked her lover, Ali.
A7 Dm Dm6
She sighed and she cried as the door opened wide,
Am E7 Am
And in walked her lover, Ali.

Am E7
Now, Ali was handsome and tall,
Dm Am
He was able to outlast them all.
A7 Dm
That is, so he thought, till one day he was caught
Am E7 Am
By the Sultan, who crushed his left ball.
A7 Dm Dm6
That is, so he thought, till one day he was caught
Am E7 Am
By the Sultan, who crushed his left ball.

Am E7
Zuleika knew naught of his fate,
Dm Am
As quickly she opened her gate.
A7 Dm
But then she recoiled, seeing his manhood spoiled,
Am E7 Am
And said, "Ali, you're now second-rate."
A7 Dm Dm6
But then she recoiled, seeing his manhood spoiled,
Am E7 Am
And said, "Ali, you're now second-rate."

Am E7
She threw out the key once again,
Dm Am
Expecting her love, Suleiman.
A7 Dm
She sighed and she cried, and she virtually died,
Am E7 Am
As in walked a whole caravan.
A7 Dm Dm6
She sighed and she cried, and she virtually died,
Am E7 Am
As in walked a whole caravan.

Am E7
The leader then bowed his head low,
Dm Am
And waited, her wishes to know.
A7 Dm
"The most of you stay," Zuleika did say,
Am E7 Am
But the children and camels must go.
A7 Dm Dm6
"The most of you stay," Zuleika did say,
Am E7 Am
"But the children and camels must go."

Am E7
What happened is hard to believe,
Dm Am
When children and camels did leave.
A7 Dm
The Arabian nights never saw such wild sights,
Am E7 Am
As the tricks she had hid up her sleeve.
A7 Dm Dm6
The Arabian nights never saw such wild sights,
Am E7 Am
As the tricks she had hid up her sleeve.

Am E7
When each one had taken his turn,
Dm Am
Still Zuleika's passion did burn.
A7 Dm
The chief bowed his head and wearily said,
Am E7 Am
"Let the children and camels return."
A7 Dm Dm6
The chief bowed his head and wearily said,
Am E7 Am
"Let the children and camels return."

THE WINNIPEG WHORE

She wanted my money but all she got was hot dick.
Norfolk Jack

C G7
My first trip up the Chip - pe - wa Riv - er,
C D7 G F G7
My first trip to Can - a - di - an shores; There I met a
C Am Em D7 G7 C
fair young maid - en, Known to all as the Win - ni - peg Whore.

C G7
She said, "Welcome to Winnipeg, mister."
C D7 G
Rubbed her ass against my knee.
F G7 C Am
Said I could have it if I cared to,
Em D7 G7 C
Dollar and a half would be her fee.

C G7
Some were fiddling, some were piddling,
C D7 G
Some were fucking on the bar room floor,
F G7 C Am
But I was spending my money happily,
Em D7 G7 C
Laying it into the Winnipeg whore.

C G7
Fucked her once and I fucked her once again,
C D7 G
Then I fucked her one time more.
F G7 C Am
She gave a shout and then she fainted –
Em D7 G7 C
That was the end of the Winnipeg whore.

Basic Guitar Chords

BASIC GUITAR CHORDS

Key to symbols employed in this chart:

- P = Primary Bass String
- A = Alternate Bass String
- × = String Not to Be Played
- ○ = Open String to Be Played
- (3) = Finger May Be Moved for Alternate Bass
- ▬ = Barre

Note: The number immediately to the right of some of the barres indicates the fret at which the barre is placed.

The diagrams of some chords may differ here from the way they were pictured elsewhere in this book. These are alternate fingerings—all are equally correct.

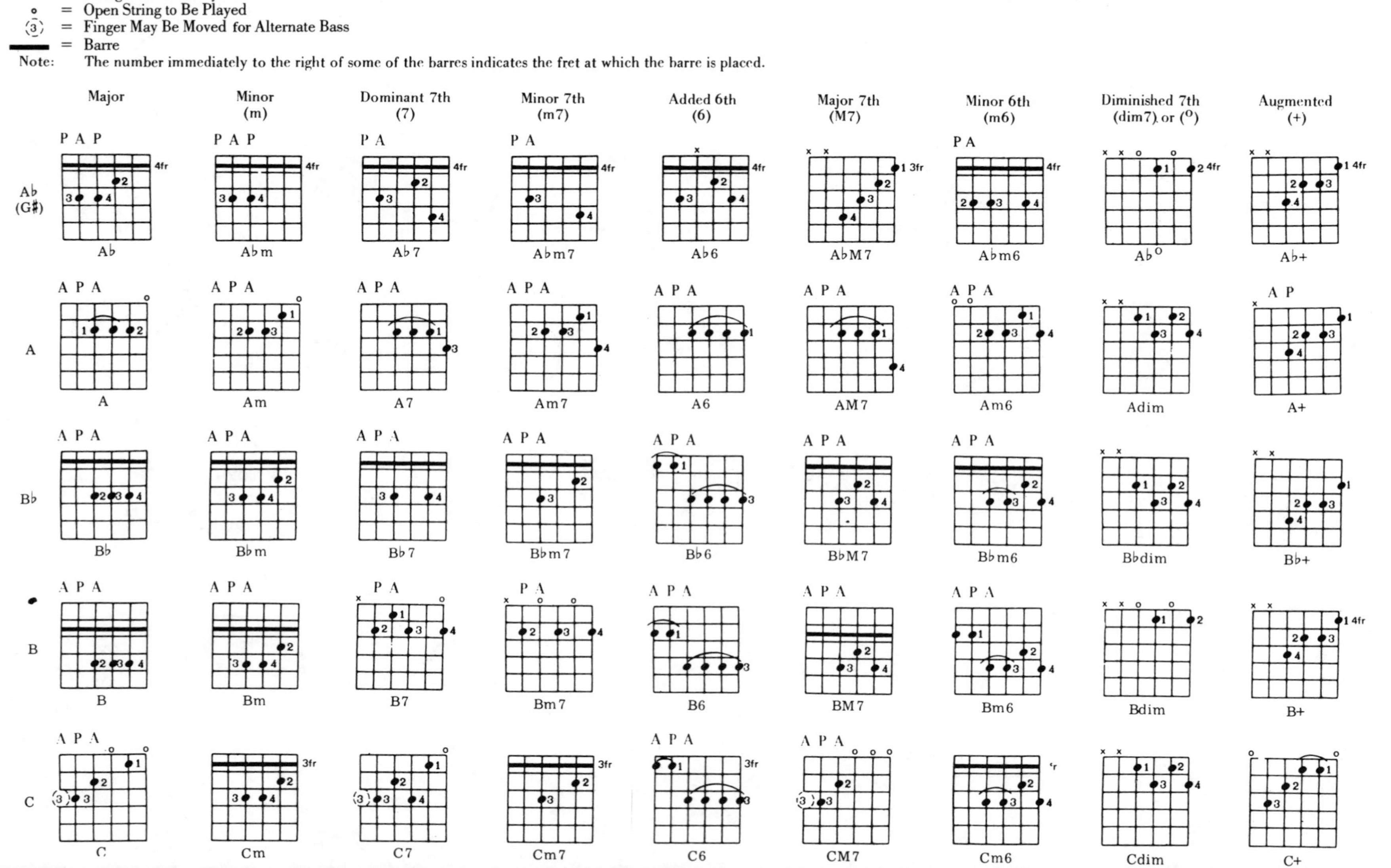

Major
Minor (m)
Dominant 7th (7)
Minor 7th (m7)
Added 6th (6)
Major 7th (M7)
Minor 6th (m6)
Diminished 7th (dim7) or (°)
Augmented (+)
A♭ (G♯)
A
B♭
B
C
A♭ A♭m A♭7 A♭m7 A♭6 A♭M7 A♭m6 A♭° A♭+
A Am A7 Am7 A6 AM7 Am6 Adim A+
B♭ B♭m B♭7 B♭m7 B♭6 B♭M7 B♭m6 B♭dim B♭+
B Bm B7 Bm7 B6 BM7 Bm6 Bdim B+
C Cm C7 Cm7 C6 CM7 Cm6 Cdim C+

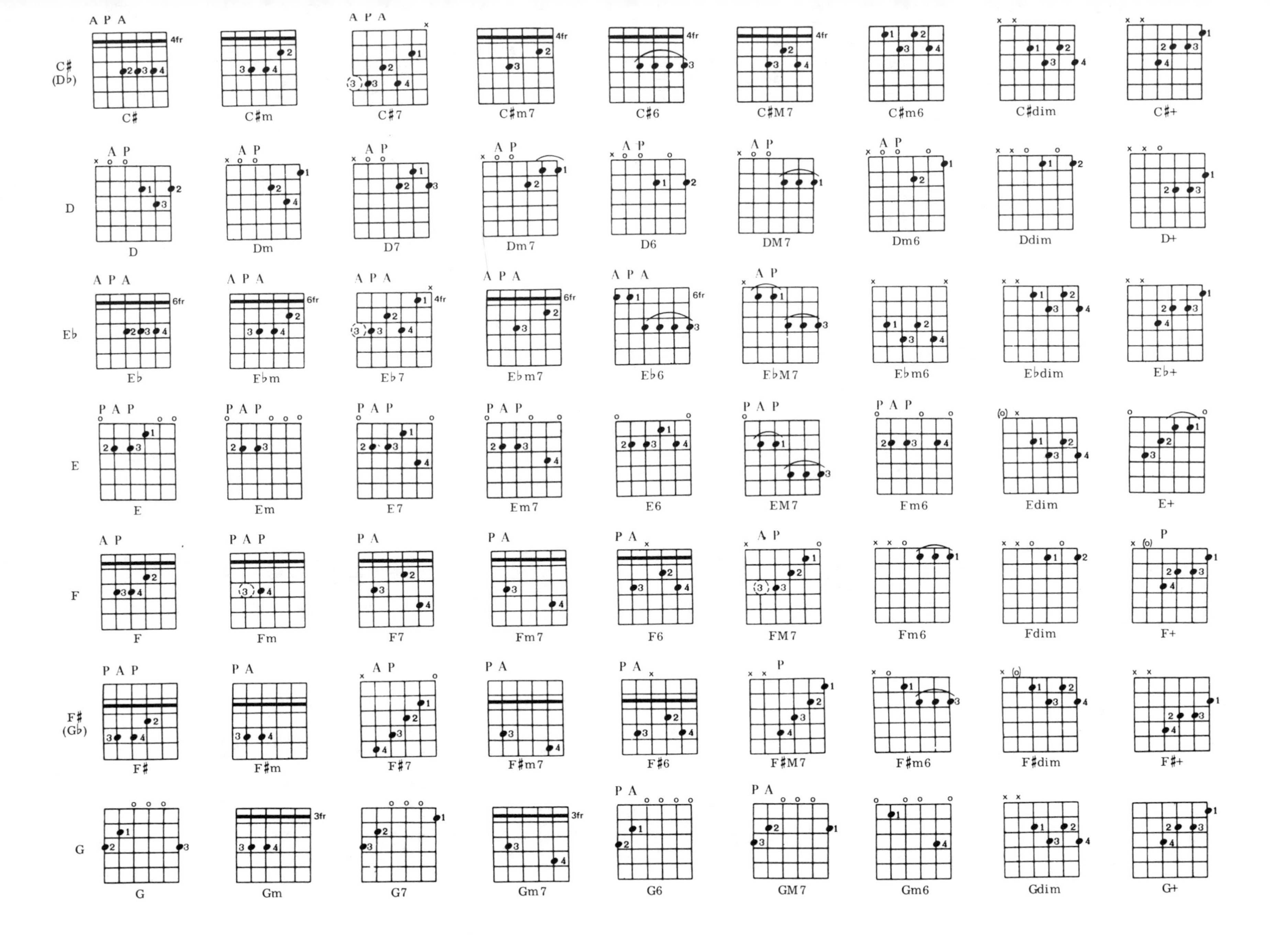
C♯ (D♭)
C♯ C♯m C♯7 C♯m7 C♯6 C♯M7 C♯m6 C♯dim C♯+
D
D Dm D7 Dm7 D6 DM7 Dm6 Ddim D+
E♭
E♭ E♭m E♭7 E♭m7 E♭6 E♭M7 E♭m6 E♭dim E♭+
E
E Em E7 Em7 E6 EM7 Fm6 Edim E+
F
F Fm F7 Fm7 F6 FM7 Fm6 Fdim F+
F♯ (G♭)
F♯ F♯m F♯7 F♯m7 F♯6 F♯M7 F♯m6 F♯dim F♯+
G
G Gm G7 Gm7 G6 GM7 Gm6 Gdim G+